Biological Clocks in Medicine and Psychiatry

BIOLOGICAL CLOCKS
IN
MEDICINE AND PSYCHIATRY

By

CURT PAUL RICHTER, Ph.D.

Professor Emeritus of Psychobiology
The Johns Hopkins Medical School
Baltimore, Maryland

CHARLES C THOMAS PUBLISHER
Springfield • Illinois • U.S.A.

Published and Distributed Throughout the World by
CHARLES C THOMAS • PUBLISHER
BANNERSTONE HOUSE
301-327 East Lawrence Avenue, Springfield, Illinois, U.S.A.
NATCHEZ PLANTATION HOUSE
735 North Atlantic Boulevard, Fort Lauderdale, Florida, U.S.A.

With THOMAS BOOKS *careful attention is given to all details of manufacturing and design. It is the Publisher's desire to present books that are satisfactory as to their physical qualities and artistic possibilities and appropriate for their particular use.* THOMAS BOOKS *will be true to those laws of quality that assure a good name and good will.*

Printed in the United States of America
Q-1

Preface

As DELIVERED in 1959, the first of two lectures dealt with biological clocks in animals, the second with biological clocks in man. For the present purposes the material of these two lectures has now been reorganized in an effort to obtain a more logical sequence. Little has been added even though in the interim we have carried on further intensive research in this area. Brief accounts of different parts of the material of these lectures were communicated in a paper on "Biological Clocks in Medicine and Psychiatry: Shock-Phase Hypothesis" in 1960;[1] in a paper read before the American Philosophical Society in Philadelphia in 1961; and in the annual Percival Bailey Lecture in Chicago in 1963. The results of the intensive research on two special aspects of biological clocks will appear soon as monographs—one on "The 24- or nearly 24-Hour Clock in Rats and Man"; the other on "Biological Clocks and the Endocrine Glands."

Support for these studies came originally (1923-1940) from the Rockefeller Foundation through grants made to Adolf Meyer, former Director of the Henry Phipps Psychiatric Clinic, The Johns Hopkins Hospital; it now comes from the National Science Foundation (1956 to present) and the National Institutes of Health (1952 to present) and the National Council on Alcoholism, Inc. (1959-1960).

Many colleagues have helped with suggestions and criticisms in the preparation of these lectures. I want to express my thanks to them. I am particularly indebted, however, to Dr. Edwards A. Park, Professor Emeritus of Pediatrics in the Johns Hopkins Medical School, and Dr. Katherine K. Rice for their ever-continuing help and encouragement. I am also indebted to my wife for her help in proofreading of the manuscript; to Mrs. Margaret Brunner and Mrs. Joy Rexroad for their help in preparation of the manuscript and illustrations; and to Mrs. Isabelle A. Powell for her help in collecting case histories of patients with periodic illnesses (1957).

The material on which these lectures are based was originally organized during a year (1957-1958) spent at the Institute for Advanced Study in Princeton.

C. P. R.

The Thomas William Salmon
Memorial Lectures

The Salmon Lectures of the New York Academy of Medicine were established in 1931 as a memorial to Thomas William Salmon, M.D. and for the advancement of the objectives to which his professional career had been wholly devoted.

Dr. Salmon died in 1927, at the age of 51, after a career of extraordinary service in psychiatric practice and education, and in the development of a world-wide movement for the better treatment and prevention of mental disorders, and for the promotion of mental health.

Following his death, a group of his many friends organized a committee for the purpose of establishing one or more memorials that might serve to preserve and pass on to future generations some of the spirit and purpose of his supremely noble and useful life. Five hundred and ninety-six subscriptions were received, three hundred and nineteen from physicians.

For the purpose of giving lasting quality to the lectures as a memorial to Dr. Salmon and of extending their usefulness, it was stipulated that the lectures should each be published in a bound volume. This volume is one of that series.

The Salmon Committee is composed of the following members:

Contents

Biological Clocks in Medicine and Psychiatry

Introduction

DURING THE PAST thirty years I have visited famous clock and watch exhibits in London, Madrid, Vienna and in this country. What I saw impressed me with the great ingenuity displayed thoughout the ages by man in his efforts to measure time. Until the recent development of technological skills, clocks and watches were the most intricate, delicate mechanical devices that had been made by man.

I bring this up because—if the findings and conclusions reported in these lectures are correct—all human beings and most animals harbor not only one but many timing devices that are no less impressive in their way than are those made by man—in fact, in some instances they may be even more impressive.

These timing devices merit great interest, not only because of their remarkable nature, but, as will be seen, because of the light that they may throw on the functioning of various organs of the body, particularly of different parts of the brain, and on normal and abnormal behavior of the total organism.

During a long career in biological psychological research I have had the good fortune to discover the existence of a number of timing devices in animals— chiefly in the ordinary laboratory Norway rat. Through my long association with the Johns Hopkins Hospital and the Phipps Psychiatric Clinic I have also had the opportunity of seeing the operation of many of such timing devices in man.

In this way—and aided by reports of periodic biologic phenomena and periodic illnesses in the literature—I have succeeded in making a sizable collection of timing devices of both animals and man—a small part of which will now be put on exhibit.

Before viewing this exhibit we should first look at a list of timing devices that has been prepared for this occasion. See Table I, Parts I and II. Part I lists timing devices or clocks found in Norway rats (normals and those that have been subjected to various forms of experimental interferences), desert rats, pocket mice, and ground squirrels. Part II lists timing devices found in normal man, and in man suffering from various forms of periodic illnesses (somatic or primarily mental and emotional). These timing devices are listed in order of increasing lengths of units in which they measure time.

For many persons, physicians as well as laymen, the concept of biological timing devices is limited to the regular recurrence of menstruation. Since this function is only one among many that are thus regulated, we are placing quite a variety of clocks on exhibit and demonstrating their respective time-keeping abilities by corresponding graphic records. It should be pointed out that the examples given are only a few

TABLE I—PART I

Biological Clocks or Timing Devices in Rats and Other Rodents

(Listed in order of lengths of clock units)

Norway Rats		Desert Rats	Pocket Mice	Ground Squirrels
Normal	*After Various Forms of Experimental Interference*	*Normal*	*Normal*	*Blinded*
1½-2 hours (3-4 hours)				
24—or nearly 24—hours (12—or nearly 12—hours)				
4 or 5 days				7-13 days
12-14 days	10-14 days			
14-22 days				14-15 days
	16-20 days			
22 days	22 days			
	30 days	35-45 days		
	40-60 days		24-84 days	
	76-124 days			
	160-180 days			
				365—or nearly 365 days

among many available to us. They should suffice for our present purposes.

Before proceeding further it might be well to state more clearly what is encompassed by the term "biological clocks." These are inherent timing devices that function quite independently of external events—and to a large extent of internal events; on the other hand they are not chronometers that can be consulted at any time; they must be thought of more as alarm or timing devices—that register intervals. The account of our experiments and observations on the different kinds of clocks and the following discussions should

TABLE I—PART II

BIOLOGICAL CLOCKS OR TIMING DEVICES IN MAN

(Listed in order of lengths of clock units)

Normal	Periodic Illnesses	
	Somatic	Mental or Emotional
1½-2 hours Infants—45 min.	12 hours	
24 hours	24 hours	24 hours
	48 hours	48 hours
		5 days
	7 days	6 days
	14 days	14 days
	17-19 days	
	20-21 days	21 days
	24-25 days	
28 days	26-30 days	30 days
		40 days
	50-60 days	52 days 100 days
	4-5 months	
280 days		
		1 year
		1¼ years
		2 years
		10 years

give a better idea of the nature of biological clocks.

I should also like to explain how the various clocks in animals and man were collected. In rats, spontaneous running activity (as measured in revolving drums) has been found to be the best tool for the detection of the existence of internal timing devices. This function has proved to be a reliable "hand" of many clocks. Fortunately in my earliest experiments,[2] in 1919, on spontaneous activity of rats I started the practice of taking records of daily running activity, food* and water intake over long periods—many months or even years—and I have continued this routine procedure in all subsequent experiments no matter in what field— endocrinology, neurology, or nutrition. Such records on many thousands of normal and experimental rats have revealed the presence of a large number of different clocks.

The collection of clocks of man was made chiefly from observations on patients suffering from various kinds of periodic illnesses—some somatic, others primarily mental or emotional. Observations on the former groups of patients were obtained from hospitals and clinics which kept regular records, with readings taken one or more times each day, of many functions—body temperature, pulse rate, urine output, blood counts, etc. over long periods of time. Observations on the latter group of patients were obtained chiefly from psychiatric hospitals or clinics, or state institutions in which daily charts of behavior, mood, etc. were kept over long periods of time. For the purposes of this study the best records in either category are

culled from the latter years of the last, and early years of the present century, before the wide-spread use of antibiotics, tranquilizers and other agents, reduced interest in taking long term records or obliterated all signs of the presence of clocks in many instances.

Pilcz,[3] Gjessing,[4] and Menninger-Lerchenthal[5] have collected histories of many patients with various kinds of periodic mental and emotional illnesses; Reimann,[6] has collected histories of many patients with somatic illnesses. In making my collection I have drawn heavily from all of these sources. Histories on well over 1000 patients are now at hand.

On our tour of the exhibits we shall start with clocks that have been found in rats and a few other rodents; then proceed to clocks found in man. I shall describe conditions under which each clock manifests itself; and then review what knowledge we have, if any, of its location and underlying mechanisms.

After having viewed this exhibit we shall summarize our knowledge about biological clocks in general: specificity of length of units in which each measures time; conditions conducive to their appearance; their common underlying mechanisms; light they throw on functions of various organs of the body and particularly of various parts of the brain; roles played by the clocks in periodic somatic and mental illnesses; and finally, roles played by the clocks in every-day life in control and regulation of autonomic functions and of thinking and emotions in normal individuals.

---

* Food mixture recommended by Dr. E. V. Mc-Collum in 1922 has remained the same throughout the years: Graham flour 72.5 percent, casein 10.0 percent, butter 5.0 percent, skim milk powder 10.0 percent, calcium carbonate 1.5 percent and sodium chloride 1.0 percent.

Exhibits of Biological Clocks or Timing Devices

A. Clocks Found in Normal Rats

THE COLUMN at the left in Part I of Table I lists the clocks found in normal rats in order of the lengths of units in which they measure time.

ONE AND ONE-HALF TO TWO HOUR CLOCK. Let us start with the one and one-half to two hour clock that manifests itself in the starved rat by regularly recurring bursts of gross bodily activity. Figure 1 shows a drawing of a cage of the type we first used for re-

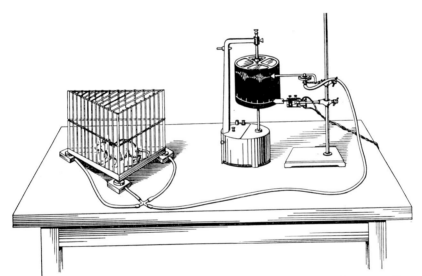

Figure 1. Stationary activity cage and kymograph used for recording short periods of activity[2] (redrawn by Munn[8]).

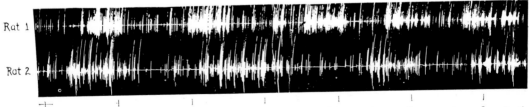

Figure 2. Smoked drum record of spontaneous gross bodily activity of two starved rats in stationary cages. Time in hours.[2]

7

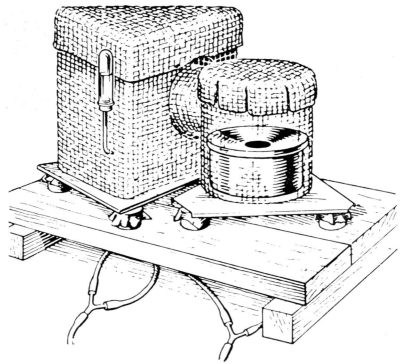

Figure 3. Double cage used in obtaining separate records of spontaneous gross bodily activity and time spent in eating[2] (redrawn by Munn[8]). Tunnel entrance to food cup does not touch side of large cage.

cording activity.* The cage rests on three tambours. Every movement of the rat, however slight, is transmitted pneumatically to a Marey tambour and so to the smoked drum. Figure 2 shows records taken on two rats from 10 P.M. to 4:30 A.M. The rats had been without food since early afternoon. For Rat #1

the bursts of activity, each lasting about forty-five minutes, recurred at regular intervals of one and one-half hours; for Rat #2 the intervals were one and three-quarters hours long.

The double cage shown in Figure 3 made it possible to obtain separate records of gross bodily activity in a main cage and of eating times in a smaller separately supported and registering cage containing a food-cup. Only once during each activity period the rat entered the food-cage and ate as indicated in Figure 4. Particularly noteworthy is the long period of increasing activity preceding the rat's entrance into the food-cage. Grooming accounts for the

* This figure and the immediately following records are taken from my doctoral thesis published in 1921[2] and from my paper on "Animal Behavior and Internal Drives," in 1926.[7] These cycles of activity may not seem very impressive, but to me they are still very exciting; they were the first fruits collected about forty-four years ago, within a short time after my venture into research. This finding was the start of my still persisting interest in cyclic phenomena.

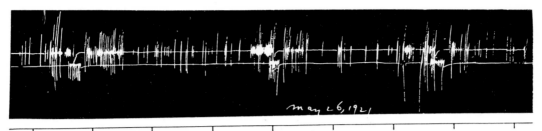

Figure 4. Smoked drum record of gross bodily activity in triangular cage (*top*) and in food cage (*bottom*). See Fig. 3. Time in hours.[2]

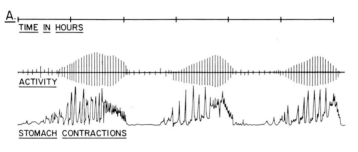

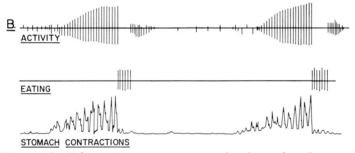

Figure 5. Schematic representation of relationship between periods of spontaneous gross bodily activity and stomach contractions: "A" for a starved rat; "B" for a rat with access to food, also showing activity in cage containing food-cup. Time in hours.[2]

activity markings subsequent to eating. A direct relationship was thus established directly between the periods of spontaneous activity and of feeding; and indirectly between the periods of activity and hunger contractions which are known to occur periodically with great regularity at this same rate in a starved animal. Figure 5 shows a schematic representation of this relationship; "A" for a starved rat and "B" for a rat with access to food. In "A" we see that progressively as stomach activity increases in intensity from tonic to clonic contractions, then finally to tetanic contractions, the animal becomes

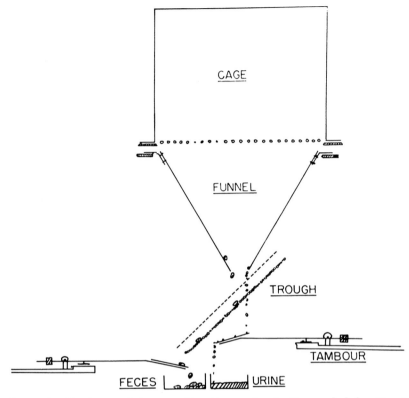

Figure 6. Device used in recording times of urination and defecation.[7]

more and more active. The subsequent sudden cessation of stomach contractions is followed by total inactivity of the animal until the start of the next series of tonic contractions of the stomach. "B" shows a similar relationship except that now at the start of the tetanic contractions—that in human beings are felt as "hunger"—the rat enters the food-cage and eats. The interrelationship between gross bodily activity and stomach contractions is illustrated with actual records in our exhibition of clocks in human beings. See Figure 61.

By means of the device shown in the drawing in Figure 6 separate records were obtained of urination and defecation times. It was found that these func-

tions also are quite regular, as may be seen in Figures 7 and 8 respectively. Urination occurred at intervals of three to four hours; defecation at slightly longer intervals. Whether the clocks governing these functions are located in the central nervous system or peripherally in the bladder or rectum, or in a relationship between these organs and the brain, we do not know.

THE TWENTY-FOUR- OR NEARLY TWENTY-FOUR-HOUR CLOCK. The next clock that we shall look at measures time in units of twenty-four- or nearly twenty-four-hours. It is probably one of the most important of all biological clocks; certainly it has received far more attention than any of the other clocks,

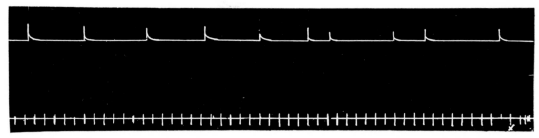

Figure 7. Smoked drum records showing times of urination in a normal rat. Time in half hour periods.[7]

Figure 8. Smoked drum record showing times of defecation in a normal rat. Time in hours.[7]

not only from physiologists, mammologists, ornithologists and entomologists, but even from botanists. In recent years conferences dealing chiefly with the twenty-four- or nearly twenty-four-hour clock have been held here and abroad, perhaps the most noteworthy being the one held at Cold Spring Harbor in 1959 under the auspices of the Long Island Biological Station.[9] Johnson[10, 11] and Rawson[12, 13] at Harvard, Bünning at Tübingen,[14] Aschoff at Heidelberg,[15] Pittendrigh[16] and Bruce[17] at Princeton, Brown at Northwestern,[18] Halberg at Minnesota,[19] and Harker at Cambridge,[20] have all made important contributions to this subject. Since it will not be possible to review these studies—made on plants, insects, birds and mammals—I shall limit myself to presenting some of my own records of the twenty-four-hour clock in the rat. These records will be presented in some detail since they illus-

trate many of the most important features of living clocks in general.

In the Norway rat the twenty-four- or nearly twenty-four-hour clock manifests itself most clearly in spontaneous running activity, which can be registered in a revolving drum.[21] Figure 9 shows the front aspects of five stands of such cages used for these observations. Figure 10 shows a close-up view of one of these cages, which is actually nothing more than a modified squirrel cage, consisting of a revolving drum, cyclometer, microswitch, and a purposely small living compartment containing a non-spillable food-cup and a graduated 100 ml water bottle. The rat can move freely back and forth between the living compartment and the drum and is in no way forced to run. A cyclometer attached to the front end of the axle records the total number of revolutions of the drum, while a micro-switch attached over an

Figure 9. Photograph of laboratory showing five stands of activity cages used in these experiments.

Figure 10. Close-up view of one of the cages, showing graduated water bottle, non-spillable food-cup, cyclometer and drum.

Figure 11. Photograph of two of five recorders used for these experiments.

excentric cam on the rear end of each axle makes and breaks a current that records actual time of each revolution on a continuous operation recorder, located in a room outside the animal laboratory. Figure 11 shows two such recorders. Each recorder simultaneously registers activity of twenty individual rats. The paper moves at a rate of eighteen inches per twenty-four hours. The twenty-four-hour records from each recorder are cut into their twenty component strips by means of an especially designed machine. The strips recording each animal's daily activity are mounted one under the other between lines printed one-fourth inch apart on large cardboard charts, thus giving a continuous graphic record of the twenty-four-hour distribution of each animal's activity as may be seen in Figure 12. This photograph shows the process of mounting the strips for one rat on the chart, using a hot tacking iron and photographic mounting tissue. Figure 13 shows such activity distribution records for three normal rats. Each daily record extends from noon to noon; the laboratory was completely darkened from 6 P.M. to 6 A.M. Black areas and lines indicate activity in the revolving drum. The paper moves at too slow a rate to permit separate registration of each revolution when the rats are very active. These three rats were active mainly during the twelve hours of darkness. Noteworthy are the individual differences between the three rats and the consistencies in the records of each rat from day to day—particularly in the times of onset of activity each twenty-four hours.

We were interested at the start in determining to what extent these twenty-four-hour patterns of activity are dependent on auditory, olfactory and visual stimuli.

Before presenting results it should be explained that consistently throughout the many years over which these studies extend, the rats were housed in one large laboratory which accommodated

five stands of sixteen activity cages holding a total of eighty rats. All avoidable stimuli were kept to a minimum, but many disturbances produced by record-taking, filling food-cups and water bottles, cleaning cages, etc. could of course not be eliminated. Room temperature was maintained close to 75°F the year round. Humidity was not controlled.

Removal of olfactory bulbs had no effect on activity patterns, nor did deafening (by bilateral destruction of the cochleas). In contrast, blinding (by section of optic nerves or enucleation of the eyes) however, had a remarkable effect. While some of the rats continued for some days or weeks to start running at exactly the same time each day as before blinding, just as if they could still

Figure 12. Photograph showing activity-distribution chart for one rat and illustrating process of mounting individual strips of paper from the recorder.

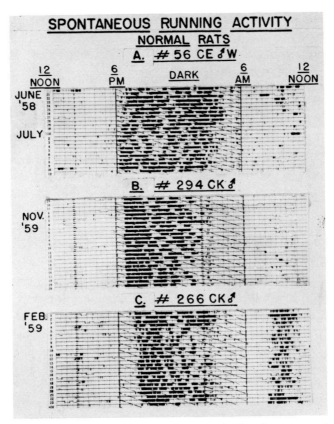

Figure 13. Activity-distribution records for three normal rats. The laboratory was in total darkness from 6 P. M. to 6 A. M.

see, sooner or later with few exceptions, all of them started running either earlier or later day after day by strikingly constant intervals. These effects are illustrated by records of three rats in Figure 14. Before blinding (EE) the first rat, 160CG♂ (Fig. 14A) began running each day about 7 P.M., that is, one hour after the start of the period of total darkness. After blinding it began running at 6 P.M., almost at once after the lights were turned off; it continued to run each day at 6 P.M. for over a month, just as though it could still recognize the difference between light and darkness.

Before blinding (EE) rat 299CF ♀ (Fig. 14B) started to run each night near 8 P.M.. After blinding it began running four minutes earlier each day for the first twenty days; after that its activity commenced by exactly twenty-two minutes earlier each successive day. Before blinding rat 301CF ♀ (Fig. 14C) started to run almost at once after the start of the dark period. Within ten days after blinding it began to run exactly twenty-three minutes later each day.

In my doctoral thesis[2] I reported that rats exposed to alternating periods of twelve hours of light and twelve hours of darkness became active each night shortly after the start of the dark period and that they continued to become active at the same time even when kept in constant darkness. At that time I observed the rats in constant darkness for periods of only ten to fourteen days. This explains my failure to observe the remarkable shifts of the onsets of activity away from the twenty-four hour period that were first observed by Johnson[10, 11] in the field mouse, and later by Rawson.[12]

It is noteworthy that blinding had very little other immediate effect on the rat, since in most cases food and water intake, body weight, total amount of running activity, and estrous cycles remained practically unchanged for the first few months.

The truly astonishing precision with which blinded rats are able to keep time is shown in the record in Figure 15. This wild rat (recently trapped in Baltimore and blinded seven weeks before the start of this record) ran precisely twenty-six minutes earlier on successive

days, with an astonishingly high degree of accuracy, as may be seen by the fact that onsets of running each day form an almost perfectly straight line. That this animal's clock kept such perfect time is particularly remarkable considering that this was a recently trapped fierce, aggressive, suspicious, wild rat that was thus being exposed daily to the many disturbances in the laboratory involved in taking records on eighty animals, cleaning cages, etc.

During the past seven years we have kept records of this type on 350 blinded rats—covering periods of over two years in some cases. In this way we have been able to determine how long these cycles persist in different animals, to what extent the clocks continue to keep time with a high degree of accuracy such as is seen in Figure 15. With very few exceptions all 350 rats gave evidence of possessing reliable twenty-four—or nearly twenty-four—hour clocks.

Before showing long term records, I must make it clear how we read such records. The record of the blinded rat

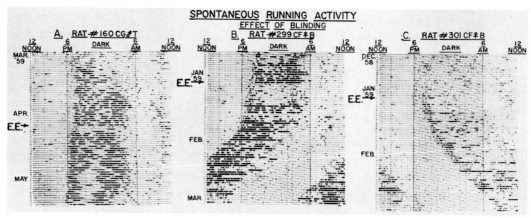

Figure 14. Activity distribution records for three rats illustrating effects produced by blinding (EE).

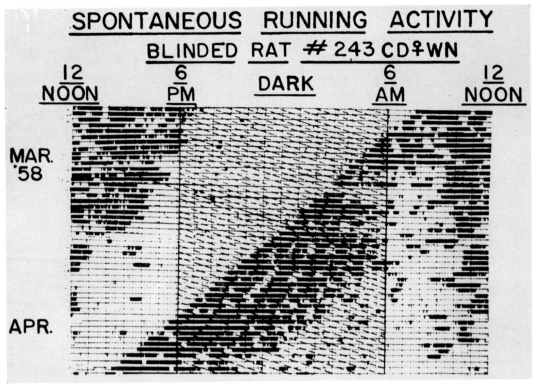

Figure 15. Activity-distribution record illustrating great accuracy of times of onsets of activity from day to day. This wild Norway (trapped in Baltimore) was blinded several weeks before the start of this record.

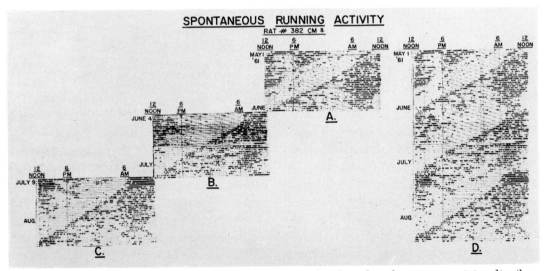

Figure 16. Records of a blinded rat illustrating methods of reading long-term activity distribution charts. At the left successive parts of this rat's chart "A," "B" and "C" are placed side-by-side, showing that the onsets of activity formed almost a perfectly straight line; at the right "D" these charts are placed one under the other, showing that in this way the onsets of activity form a series of parallel lines.

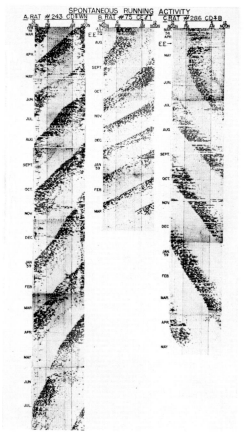

Figure 17. Long term activity-distribution charts of three rats "A" after blinding, "B" and "C" before and after blinding (EE).

382CM ♀ shown in Figure 16 illustrates this process. "A" shows approximately one month's record of activity-distribution of this rat which had been blinded seven weeks before the start of this record. The onset of activity occurred thirty-six minutes earlier each day. As the onsets of activity leave the left edge of the chart—that is when activity is commencing at noon—they appear on the following chart "B" at the right edge at noon; and in the same way they subsequently appear at the right edge of chart "C," thus producing a practically

straight line over a three and one-half month period. To conserve space these charts are mounted one under the other as in "D" where we see that as the onsets of activity leave the left edge of the chart they are picked up at the right edge forming parallel lines.

Figure 17 shows long term records of three blinded rats. Record "A" is that of a wild rat that was observed for over twenty-four months. (Records are shown here for eighteen months.) Its clock kept perfect time for the first few months, then gradually slowed down; Figure 17B shows the record of a domesticated Norway rat whose clock kept nearly perfect time over a five month period running thirty-eight minutes earlier each day. Figure 17C shows the record of another domesticated Norway rat, this time with onsets of activity occurring later each day; this clock also measured time with great accuracy.

That we are dealing here with definitely inherent clock mechanisms—that is, with clocks that are entirely independent of external influences—is demonstrated by the fact that of fifty blinded rats on record in the laboratory at any one time, some may be displaying cycles of various lengths shorter than twenty-four hours, others of various lengths longer than twenty-four hours, and others of exactly twenty-four hours—quite independently of one another and of all external conditions.

The presence and functioning of the clock can be observed in very inactive as well as in normally active or hyperactive rats. Thus, inactive rats may run only five to thirty minutes per day, but then with regularity at definite periods either longer or shorter than twenty-

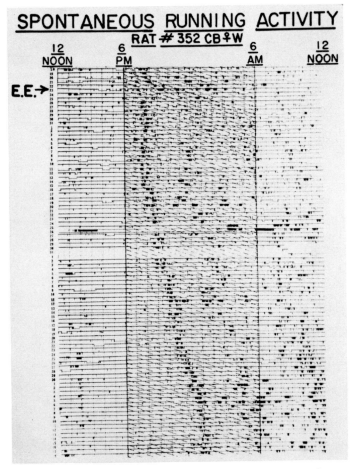

Figure 18. Activity-distribution chart of an extremely inactive rat before and after blinding (EE).

four hours each day. Figure 18 shows the record of a very inactive rat whose five to forty minute period of activity occurred five minutes later each day.

It is noteworthy that the clock manifests itself not only in activity but also in eating and drinking times, as may be seen in the record of a normal (nonblinded) rat in Figure 19. During active phases in the revolving drum cages the rats go back and forth almost continuously between the running drum, food-cup, and drinking fountain—running,

eating and drinking. The record shows clearly that this rat, as did many others, timed both the beginning and end of the periods of activity, eating and drinking. The close relationship between activity, eating and drinking times is illustrated also in the record of the blinded rat in Figure 20. From these and many similar records we know that this clock measures time in periods of twelve- or nearly twelve-hours, as well as of twenty-four- or nearly twenty-four-hours. See also in Figures 17 and 20.

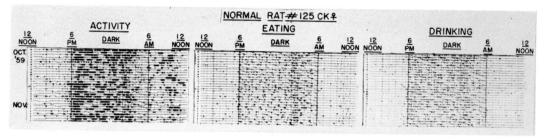

Figure 19. Record showing daily distribution of activity, feeding and drinking times of a normal rat.

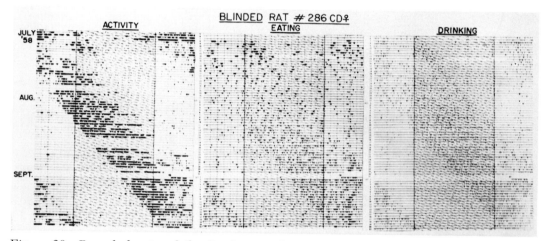

Figure 20. Record showing daily distribution of activity, feeding and drinking times of a rat blinded 100 days before start of this record.

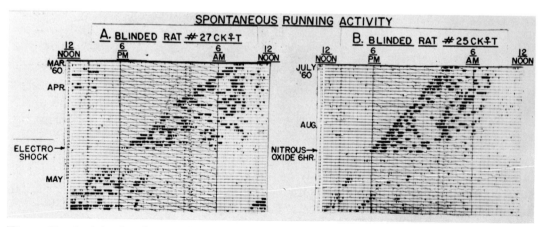

Figure 21. Activity-distribution charts from two blinded rats showing lack of effect of "A" electro-shock; and "B" nitrous oxide inhalation on the clock; also illustrating concept of the "hand" of the clock.

How can this clock be speeded up; slowed down; reset; or stopped? Blinded rats were subjected to almost every conceivable kind of metabolic, endocrinologic and neurologic interference. Increasing metabolic rate to high or decreasing it to low levels had no effect; removal of the endocrine glands—adrenals, gonads, thyroid, pineal, pancreas, pituitary—had no effect; nor did electroshock, or convulsions, or prolonged profound sleep produced by various drugs, or profound alcoholic stupor, have any effect. So far the only method found for stopping or resetting the clock is through the production of profound hypothermia: body temperature 7-4°C with cessation of respiration and heart beat for an hour or more. Thus, we see that this clock in the rat is quite as independent of all external and internal events and stimuli, as a wrist watch is of its wearer.

The fact that the various endocrine glands can be removed without affecting the clock demonstrates effectively that the clock can not reside in any of them. Exhaustive experimentation has convinced us that it must be located in the brain. In our attempts to stop or alter the functioning of the clock we have produced literally hundreds of lesions in all parts of the brains of rats and have narrowed down the site to a small area in the hypothalamus but we are not satisfied as to its exact boundaries.

Observations on the twenty-four- or nearly twenty-four-hour clock make it possible to illustrate a concept which is very important for the study of the operation of biological clocks in general—this concerns the "hand" or "hands" of the clock. Figure 21A illustrates what is meant by the "hand" of the clock. Over a period of several months the clock of this blinded rat whose record is shown at the left was measuring time in units of twenty-three hours forty-five minutes. Convulsions produced by electro-shock made it totally inactive for ten days. That the clock continued to run during this ten day interval is demonstrated conclusively by the fact that resumption of activity occurred at exactly the predicted time as if nothing had been done to the rat. Thus, we see that activity serves as the "hand" of the clock. It indicates that the clock is running and at what rate, but it is not a part of the internal mechanism and is not essential to the continued operation of the clock. It can be removed without altering the operation of the clock. Figure 21B illustrates the same concept. In this case the "hand" was removed for nine days by exposure of the rat to nitrous oxide gas for six hours. We have made several hundred such observations.

As we progress on our tour it will be seen that spontaneous running activity serves as the "hand" of many clocks in the rat as well as in the other rodents. It will presently be seen that many other functions, such as body temperature, serve as "hands" of clocks in man.

FOUR OR FIVE DAY CLOCK. This next clock which is found only in female rats measures time in units of four or five days with a high degree of accuracy. Dr. Ging H. Wang[22] working in this laboratory in 1921-23, showed that this clock manifests itself most regularly both in spontaneous running activity and vaginal smears as may be seen in

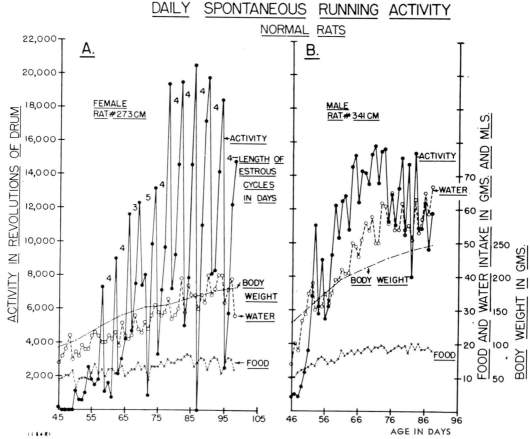

Figure 22.   Graph showing total daily spontaneous running activity, food and water intake
and body weight of (A) normal female rat; (B) normal male rat.

Figure 22A, in which ordinates show running activity, body weight and food and water intakes; abscissas age in days. Every 4th day activity reached a peak of 10-20,000 revolutions and on the three intervening days dropped to low levels of 2-4000. Ovulation occurred just before activity reached its peak, as was shown by following the stained daily vaginal smears. In some females this clock may also manifest itself in food and water intake, body weight, body temperature measurements, and nest building. Males do not possess this clock. See Figure 22B.

The functioning of this clock probably depends on a feed-back relationship between the ovary, pituitary and centers in the hypothalamus.

TWELVE-FOURTEEN DAY CLOCK. Before passing on to the next equally remarkable clock it will be necessary to give a brief description of a phenomenon known as pseudopregnancy. Various workers found that in the female rat, sterile copulation (vasectomized male)

DAILY SPONTANEOUS RUNNING ACTIVITY

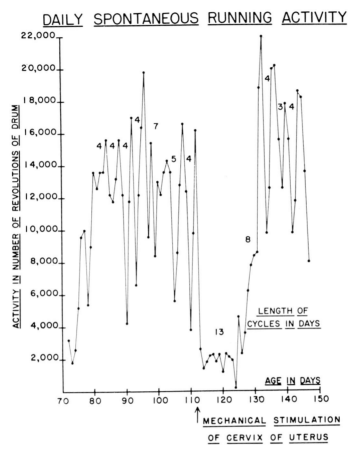

Figure 23. Record of total daily spontaneous activity showing the thirteen-day pseudopregnancy period of inactivity elicited by mechanical stimulation of the cervix.[22] (Duration of pseudopregnancy—number of days between activity peaks and between appearances of cornified cells in vaginal smears.)

or mechanical stimulation of the tip of the cervix with a glass rod induces all the symptoms of pregnancy—inactivity, greatly increased food intake, increased body weight, diestrous vaginal smears, a persistent corpus luteum, and ability of the uterus to form deciduomata. Figure 23 shows the sharp drop in spontaneous running activity during pseudopregnancy, Wang.[22] (Compare with changes that occur during pregnancy in Figure 25.)

Of interest here is that these symptoms last from twelve to fourteen days (not twenty-one to twenty-two days as in normal pregnancy) and then all functions quickly return to their normal state. The duration of pseudopregnancy would appear to be determined at least in part by the life of the corpus luteum.

Clearly, the female possesses a timing device that at least under certain circumstances measures time in units of twelve to fourteen days with a high degree of constancy.

Of special interest here is the fact that the phenomenon of pseudopregnancy can be elicited not only by sterile copulation or stimulation of the tip of the cervix but also by a great variety of other forms of stimulation and conditions not in any way related to the function of reproduction. Following is a list of various forms of stimulation which result in the manifestation of pseudopregnancy:

1. Stimulation concerned directly or indirectly with the specific phenomenon of reproduction

   S t e r i l e copulation (Long and Evans,[23] 1922; Haterius,[24] 1933).

   Mechanical and electrical stimulation of cervix (Long and Evans,[23] 1922; Haterius,[24] 1933; Meyer, Leonard, and Hisaw,[25] 1929; Shelesnyak,[26] 1931).

   Nursing (Long and Evans,[23] 1922; Selye and McKeown,[27] 1933).

   Injection of pituitary or placental hormone (Brouha,[28] 1927; Teel,[29] 1926).

   Injection of acetylcholine into pituitary (Taubenhaus and Soskin,[30] 1941).

2. Stimulation that produces stress and has nothing to do with reproduction.

   Trauma to intestine (Swingle *et al.,*[31] 1951).

   Injection or administration of noxious substances:

   Tissue homogenates (Swingle *et al.,*[31] 1951);

   Copper sulfate (intravenous) (Dury and Bradbury,[32] 1942);

Formalin (Selye and McKeown,[27] 1935; Swingle *et al.,*[33] 1951);

Silver nitrate to nasal membrane (Rosen and Shelesnyak,[34] 1937);

Chloroform (Swingle *et al.,*[32] 1951).

Injection of high amounts of drugs or hormones:

Alloxan (Swingle *et al.,*[33] 1951).

Insulin (Swingle *et al.*[33]);

Arterenol (Swingle *et al.*[33]);

Epinephrine (Swingle *et al.*[33]).

Direct electrical stimulation of skull (Harris,[35] 1937).

3. Stress leading to debilitation:

   Adrenalectomy (Swingle *et al.,*[31] 1951).

   Starvation and vitamin deficiency (Selye and McKeown,[27] 1935).

   Feeding of high amounts of thyroid extract (Weichert and Boyd,[36] 1933).

This list thus indicates that the phenomenon of pseudopregnancy may be elicited in several different ways: 1) stimulation of various parts of the reproductive system; 2) stimulation of many different non-specific and specific stress mechanisms; and 3) general debilitations induced through several different maneuvers.

Why it should be twelve to fourteen days in length with such a high degree of constancy is not clear. In previous papers[37, 38] it was suggested that this length represents an even multiple of estrous cycles taken as 4.4 days (or 4.5 days) as follows:

1. 4.4
2. 8.8
3. 13.2 pseudopregnancy
4. 17.6
5. 22.0 length of gestation

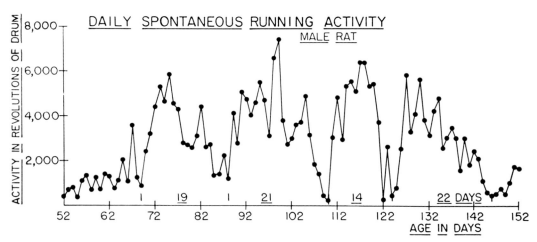

Figure 24. Record of daily total spontaneous activity showing fourteen to twenty-two day cycles in a male rat.[7]

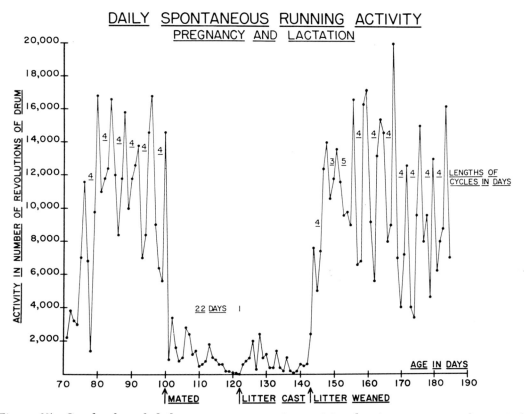

Figure 25. Graph of total daily spontaneous running activity showing twenty-two day period of pregnancy.

Pertinent here is that the life of the corpus luteum has the same length in the rat as in most species of mammals.

FOURTEEN TO TWENTY-TWO DAY CLOCK. Evidence for the existence of this clock has been found in only a few male rats. Figure 24 shows the spontaneous activity record of one of these male animals. The cycles are not regular but they are still very definite. Indication of the location of a clock within this range in males will be presented later.

TWENTY-TWO-DAY CLOCK. This "female" clock measures the lengths of gestation. It is no less remarkable than the other clocks. Figure 25 shows the effects produced by pregnancy on daily spontaneous running activity. It would also appear to represent an even multiple of the estrous cycle as 4.4 days, as was seen above. The mechanisms involved in the operation of this clock also remain unknown.

We have now seen clocks that were found in normal rats and so may proceed to clocks that make their apearance only after various forms of experimental interference.

B. Clocks found in Rats only after Various Forms of Experimental Interference

These clocks are listed in the second column of Table I, Part I, in order of the lengths of units in which they measure time.

TEN TO FOURTEEN DAY CLOCK. Here we see a phenomenon even more remarkable than the timing device which we saw measuring the length of pseudopregnancy in normal rats. In the course of work with experimentally induced diabetes insipidus, carried out in 1930, I found that after section of the pituitary stalk some female rats showed a continuous series of pseudopregnancy periods twelve to fourteen days in length, separated either by only a single day's burst of running activity with cornified cells in the vaginal smear as may be seen in Figure 26, or separated by several four to five day estrous cycles as may be seen in Figure 27. In the interval since then we have been able to produce pseudopregnancy cycles by a whole variety of forms of experimental interferences: 1) surgical removal of all except a small remnant of the thyroid

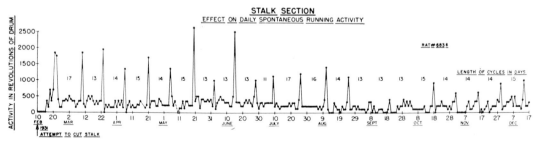

Figure 26. Graph showing single day bursts of spontaneous activity after attempted section of pituitary stalk. This was one of our first records showing this series of pseudopregnancy cycles.[37]

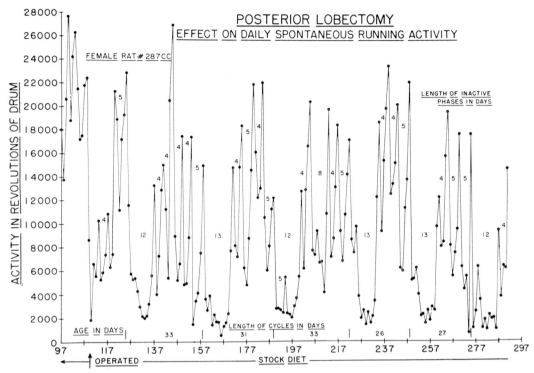

Figure 27. Graph showing cycles of spontaneous activity in a posterior lobectomized female. Each cycle consists of an active and an inactive phase. This record shows the great constancy of the lengths of the inactive phases, ranging from twelve to thirteen days; and the total lengths of the cycles, ranging from twenty-six to thirty-three days. (Lengths of inactive phases —measured from last peak that follows full four-day estrous period and cornified cells in vaginal smears to next peak that precedes normal estrous cycle and cornified cells in vaginal smear.)

gland,[38, 39, 40] or radio-iodine destruction with injections of I[131] of all except small remnants, or almost total inactivity of the thyroid produced by prolonged treatment with anti-thyroid drugs—sulfamerazine, thiourea, thiouracil, propylthiouracil or alpha-naphthyl thiourea;[40, 41] 2) removal or section of the pituitary stalk or removal of the posterior lobe;[37, 42] 3) removal of the superior colliculi with possible damage to the pretectal areas of the thalamus; 4) removal of the pretectal areas; 5) subjecting the animal to severe stress—forced swimming for forty to eighty hours[41] under a strong jet of water at a temperature of 95°F, with the experimental situation seen in Figure 28; 6) by prolonged treatment with a variety of drugs such as aminopyrine and sodium barbital, morphine sulfate,—in some instances only during treatment, in some only after the cessation of treatment and in the latter instance permanently.[43]

Figure 29 illustrates the precision with which a pseudopregnancy cycle may start and stop; and its relation to food intake and body weight.[38]

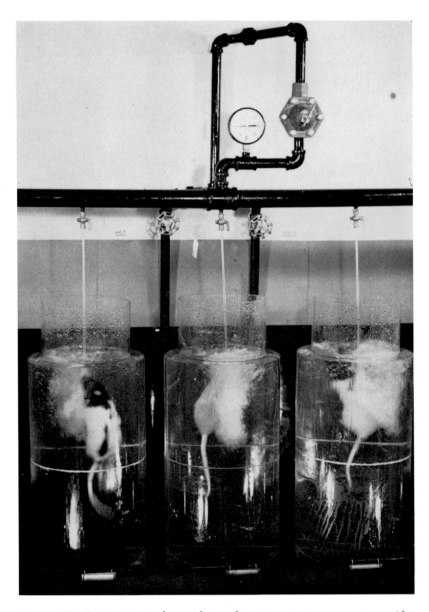

Figure 28. Swimming tanks used in subjecting rats to severe stress (fatigue, hunger, loss of sleep). A jet of water (3-4 pounds pressure) prevents floating. Water flows out of open bottom of inner cylinder and runs up and over side of outside jar.[47]

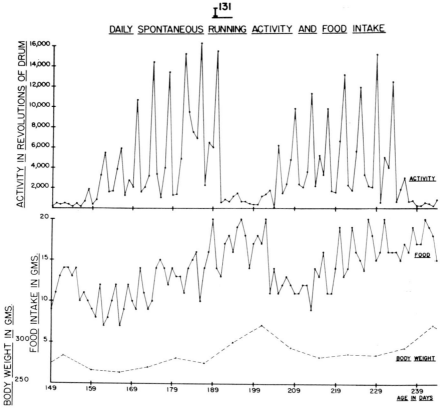

Figure 29. Graph of daily spontaneous running activity, food intake and weekly reading of body weight showing two sharply defined active and inactive phases of two cycles and their relation to cycles in food intake and body weight of a rat whose thyroid had been severely damaged by treatment with I[131]. [38]

That we actually see here a series of pseudopregnancy cycles, we were able to demonstrate in many instances by the so-called pseudopregnancy test, as may be seen in Figure 30 in the record of activity and food intake of a rat that had been forced to swim for forty-nine hours and fifty minutes at a water temperature of 95°F and a jet pressure of four pounds. This rat showed a series of four or five day activity peaks separated by fifteen to sixteen day periods of inactivity; food intake showed an inverse relationship to activity. That the inactive periods actually represented pseudopregnancy was shown by the fact that silk loops threaded through the uterine horns on the fourth day after the last activity peak of a series, resulted in the formation of large deciduomata (as demonstrated by exposing the uterus 7 days later). This means that the uterus responded just as though the rat had been impregnated.

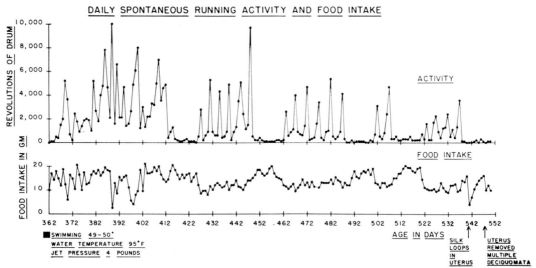

Figure 30. Graph showing series of cycles each composed of an active phase with several estrous peaks of activity and an inactive pseudopregnancy phase that followed severe swimming stress. At age 540 days silk loops threaded through the uterine horns on the fourth day after the last peak of one active phase resulted in the formation of large deciduomata which were removed seven days after the placing of the silk loops.

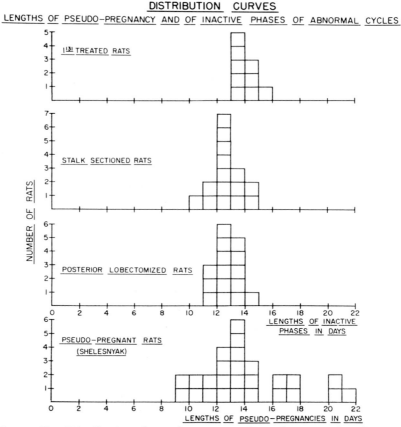

Figure 31. Distribution chart showing number of rats with relation to average lengths of inactive phases in days after: 1) treatment with I^{131}; 2) stalk section; 3) posterior lobectomy; 4) as compared with lengths of pseudopregnancy determined by Shelesnyak[44] by anatomical means.

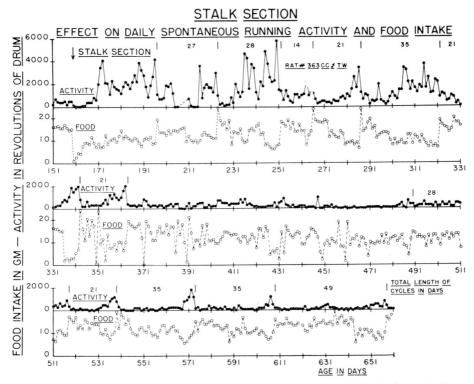

Figure 32. Graph of total daily spontaneous running activity and food intake showing irregular bursts in running activity and food intake in a male rat in which the pituitary stalk had been sectioned.

The frequency-distribution chart in Figure 31 shows the number of rats with relation to the average lengths of inactive periods for nine I[131] treated rats, fifteen stalk sectioned rats, fifteen posterior lobectomized rats; also for single pseudopregnancy periods in twenty-six females as determined by Shelesnyak.[44] It will be seen that the lengths of the inactive pseudopregnancy periods were very much the same.

Attention must be drawn here to the great constancy of the length of these inactive periods in any one rat; and to the fact that once established these inactive periods persist throughout the rest of the rat's life.

It is noteworthy that none of the forms of interference (thyroidectomy, stalk section, posterior lobectomy, treatment with sulfa drugs or anti-thyroids, etc.), which released these inactive periods with such regularity in females released them in any male. However, that some of these operations, most notably stalk section and posterior lobectomy, do affect some clock mechanisms in male rats can be seen in the record in Figure 32 which shows sharply marked and occasionally regularly recurring fluctuations in food intake and activity after stalk section.

Lengths of cycles within the pseudopregnancy range were observed in rats

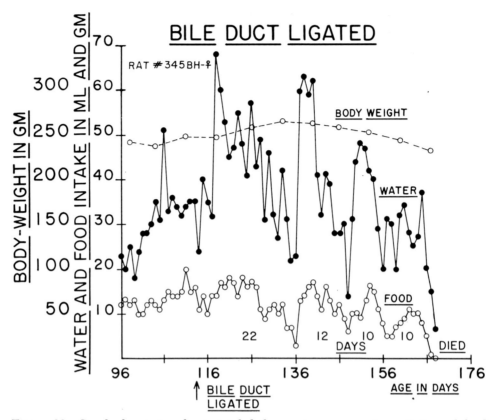

Figure 33. Graph showing cycles in total daily spontaneous running activity and food intake of a rat in which the bile duct had been ligated and sectioned.

in which the bile duct had been doubly ligated and cut as may be seen in Figure 33.[45] In this female the proximal end of the bile duct became very much distended with bile secretion, reaching the size of a tennis ball. That this form of interference releases a timing mechanism is clearly demonstrated in this record.

A few rats failed to make beneficial selections on our full self-selection diet (access to 6 electrolytes in solution in separate containers, a fat, a protein, a carbohydrate, and seven vitamins in solution in separate containers). These animals did not grow at a normal rate

and each of them showed cycles similar to those of the rats with ligated bile ducts, as may be seen in the activity record of a female in Figure 34.

Further evidence for the existence of a ten to fourteen day clock in experimental animals comes from another laboratory and from an entirely different field of investigation: the experimental production of arthritis in adult rats by a single inoculation of a water-in-oil emulsion containing heat-killed mycobacteria. Pearson[46] reported that the arthritis in about one-quarter of his inoculated rats followed a recurrent or fluctuating course. Figure 35 shows the record of

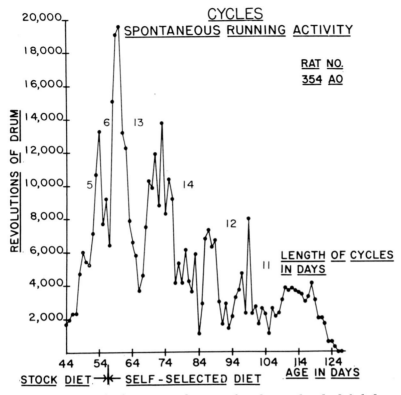

Figure 34. Graph showing cycles in a female rat that had failed to make beneficial selections from chemically purified substances all offered in separate containers.

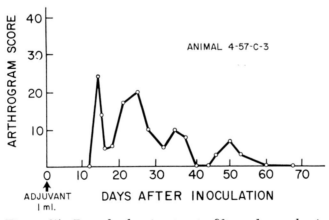

Figure 35. Records showing ten to fifteen day cycles in degree of arthritis resulting from single injection (1 ml) of adjuvant heat-killed mycobacteria (Pearson[46]).

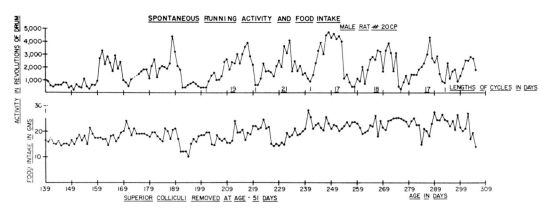

Figure 36. Graph of daily spontaneous running activity and food intake of a male rat in which both superior colliculi had been removed about ninety days earlier. Total daily spontaneous running activity showed clear-cut cycles of 17-21 days in length.

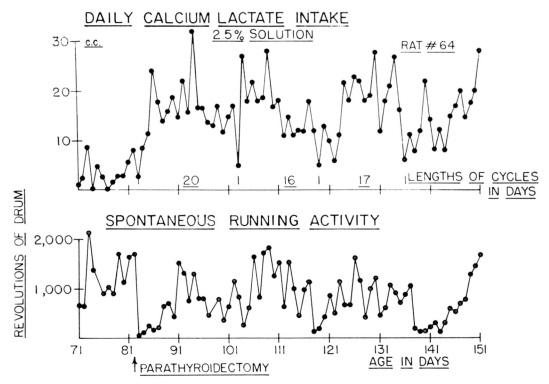

Figure 37. Graph showing total daily spontaneous running activity and voluntary intake of a 2.5 per cent solution of calcium lactate before and after parathyroidectomy.[72]

one of these rats. The arthrogram score (the sum of 4 areas of the right and left fore paws and of five areas on the hind paw showing arthritis) underwent regular fluctuations with a frequency of 12.2 days on the average. The curve closely resembled that of the rats with bile duct ligation or with a poor nutritional status (Figs. 33, 34). Of interest also is that the appearance of arthritis had a minimum latency period of at least ten days, and in nine-tenths of the rats it ranged between eleven to sixteen days.

At this place I should like to interrupt our tour of exhibits of timing devices long enough to make clear that these groupings of clocks of animals and man are for the most part only gross approximations and serve primarily to bring working order into our observations on these phenomena and as a frame-work for outlining further studies.

SIXTEEN TO TWENTY DAY CLOCK. This clock which appeared in a few normal male rats was found in most of the males and some of the females with lesions of the superior colliculi. The record of one of these animals in Figure 36 shows the presence of quite regular cycles of spontaneous running activity occurring at intervals of seventeen to twenty-one days. The average lengths of these cycles for this rat was 18.4 days.

It is noteworthy that a few parathyroidectomized males showed seventeen to twenty day cycles of spontaneous running activity and voluntary intake of a 2.5 per cent solution of calcium lactate, as may be seen in Figure 37.

TWENTY-TWO DAY CLOCK. Like the ten to fourteen day clock this clock was found only in females. I shall ask you to consider the possibility that under certain conditions the pregnancy period

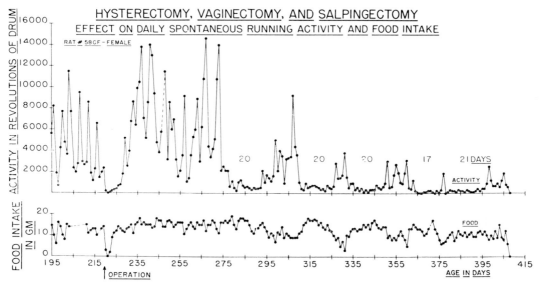

Figure 38. Graph of total daily spontaneous running activity and food intake showing seventeen to twenty-one day inactive periods that appeared in rats after hysterectomy, vaginectomy and salpingectomy, leaving the ovaries intact.

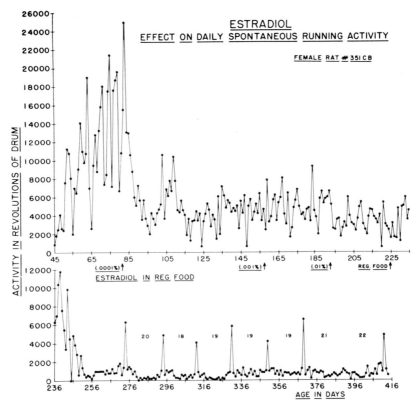

Figure 39. Graph of daily spontaneous running activity showing eighteen to twenty-two day single bursts of activity after cessation of long periods of treatment with estradiol (mixed in food).[43]

may repeat itself in series, just as the pseudopregnancy period does. This would also mean that the pregnancy clock may be made to function periodically by other stimuli than those associated with gestation.

Thus, seventeen to twenty-one day inactive periods were found in rats from which all of the female reproductive tract (vagina, uterine horns and fallopian tubes) except the ovaries had been removed. Figure 38 shows the record of such an animal.

The presence of these cycles could be explained in terms of effects of an ex-

cess of estrogen—resulting from the total absence of reproductive tissue on which it acts. Possibly in keeping with this explanation is the observation that a number of rats that for 143 days had received estradiol in their food (0.0001-0.01 per cent) showed nineteen to twenty-two day peaks of activity after the discontinuation of estradiol treatment, as may be seen in Figure 39. Of interest here also is that a number of rats that had received cortisone in their food in concentrations ranging from 0.01 to 0.5 per cent for 105 days showed sharply defined inactive periods of nine-

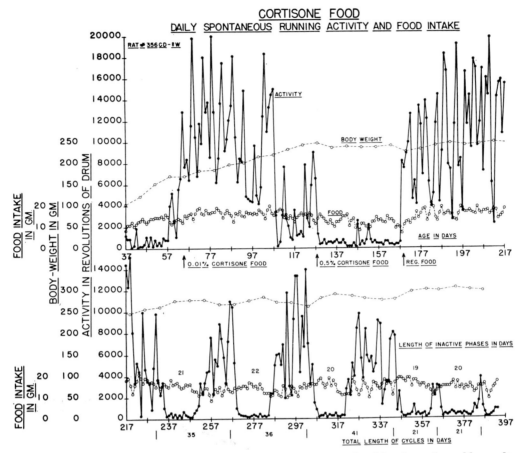

Figure 40. Graph of total daily spontaneous running activity, food intake and weekly readings of body weight of a rat before, during and after treatment with varying amounts of cortisone (mixed with food) showing series of inactive phases nineteen to twenty-two days in length subsequent to cessation of treatment.[43]

teen to twenty-two days in length subsequent to the cessation of the treatment, as may be seen in Figure 40.

It is of interest that single day bursts of activity recurred quite regularly at fifteen to twenty-two day intervals for the last six cycles in an animal that had a very large tumor—a tumor that ultimately displaced all of the hypothalamus and much of the thalamus.[41] Figure 41 shows photographs of the ventral surface of the brain of this rat and of a

sagittal section; Figure 42 shows fifteen to twenty-two day bursts of spontaneous activity that appeared 220 days before the animal was killed—that is, at a time when the tumor had not yet reached a large size. Noteworthy is that the animal was eating and drinking normal amounts of food and water and maintaining its body weight at the time it was killed—in spite of the total destruction of the hypothalamus and of part of the thalamus.

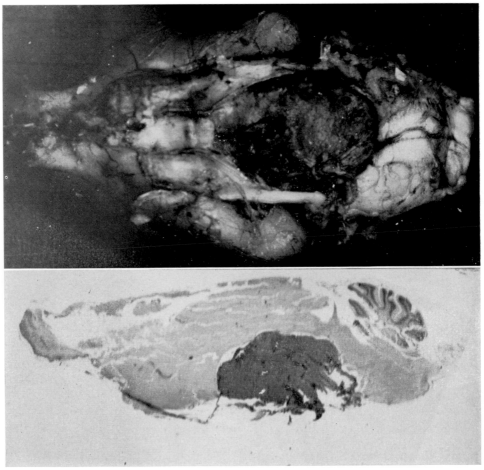

Figure 41. (*Top*) Ventral view of brain showing massive tumor. (*Bottom*) Crude sagittal section showing that tumor had obliterated hypothalamus and at least part of the thalamus.[41]

The location of this twenty to twenty-two day clock remains unknown, but it would appear to be in the brain.

THIRTY—OR NEARLY THIRTY—DAY CLOCK. Like the pseudopregnancy clock, this clock manifests itself after a great variety of forms of interference. It appeared most frequently in females after stalk section or posterior lobectomy and pretectal ablation. Figure 43 shows quite regular twenty-five to thirty-five day cycles after posterior lobectomy.

Similar cycles have been observed in rats kept on deficient diets. Figure 44 shows the activity and body weight record of a rat whose diet was restricted to lactose, casein, oleo and a solution of thiamine hydrochloride—all in separate containers. On this diet the rat lost weight at a slow rate but still remained quite active almost to the time of death on the 109th day of the diet. Of interest here is that activity did not decrease at a constant rate but in two quite clear-cut

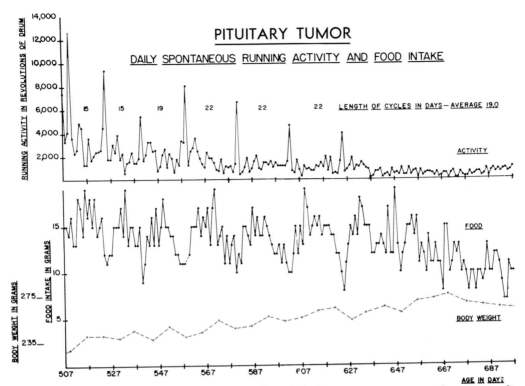

Figure 42. Graph showing single day bursts of total daily running activity and corresponding cycles of daily food intake of the rat with the large tumor pictured in Figure 41. The rat was killed 150 days after the end of the record shown in this graph. At the time the cycles were present the tumor must have been much smaller.[41]

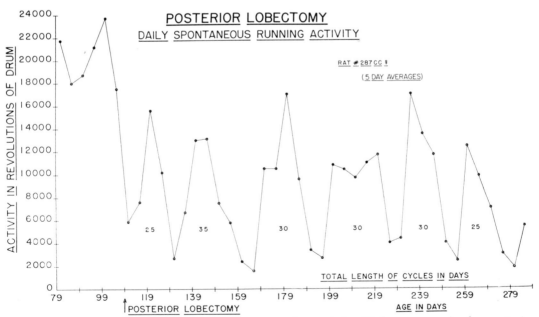

Figure 43. Graph of total daily spontaneous running activity (5 day averages) of a posterior lobectomized rat showing twenty-five to thirty-five day cycles.

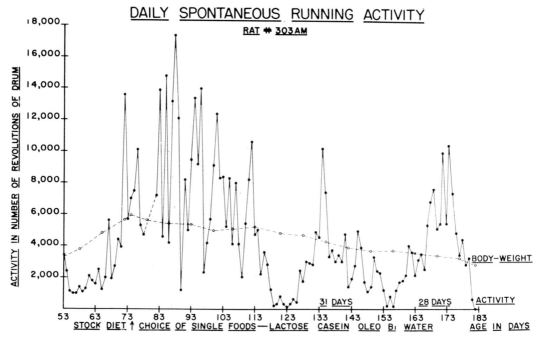

Figure 44. Graph showing thirty-one and twenty-eight day cycles of total daily spontaneous running activity of a rat whose diet was restricted to selections made from lactose, casein, oleo and thiamine hydrochloride in solution and water all offered in separate containers.

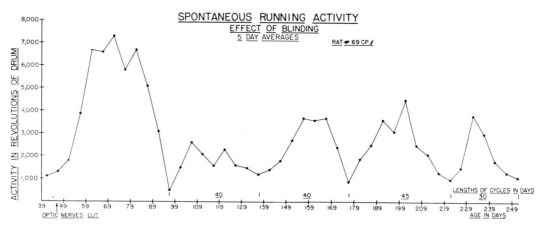

Figure 45. Graph of total daily spontaneous running activity (5 day averages) showing long cycles in a blinded male rat.

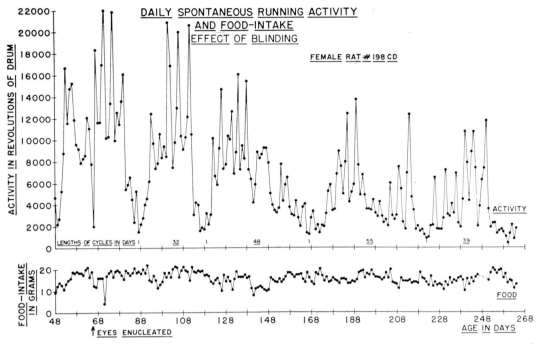

Figure 46. Graph of total daily spontaneous running activity showing long cycles that appeared after blinding in a female rat.

cycles of thirty-one and twenty-eight days in length respectively.

One of our vagotomized rats showed clear-cut cycles that averaged twenty-nine days in length. (Experiments carried on with Dr. Alan C. Woods, Jr.) A rat that had received one very large dose of phenobarbital (6 mg per 100 gm body weight) in propyl glycol also showed clear-cut but somewhat shorter cycles.

We have no idea about mechanisms underlying these thirty— or nearly thirty—day cycles; in fact we do not know that they all are evidence for the existence of just one clock.

Clocks that measure time in these approximately thirty day units were found in both males and females.

FORTY TO SIXTY DAY CLOCK. Evidence for the existence of these clocks also

came from observation on rats—males and females—that had been subjected to a variety of interferences.

These clocks were found most frequently in blinded rats. Figure 45 shows the activity cycle in a blinded male; Figure 46 in a blinded female.

Similar cycles were obtained in a few castrated wild rats. In contrast to domesticated rats, wild rats do not become almost totally inactive after castration, but remain essentially normally active. As will be seen in Figure 47 some of these may show cycles of thirty-five to forty days in length.

Severe acute stress also may bring out long cycles that persist throughout the rest of the rat's life. These cycles appeared almost exclusively in wild rats—males and females. Severe stress was

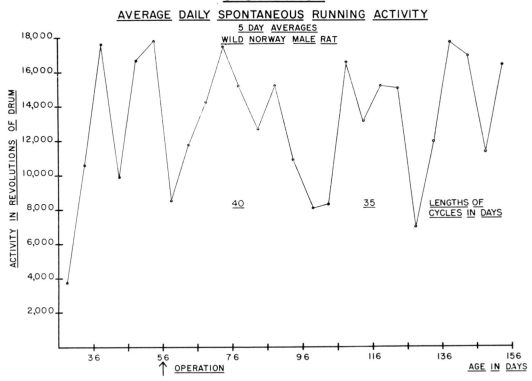

Figure 47. Graph of total daily spontaneous running activity of a castrated wild male rat showing thirty-five and forty day cycles.

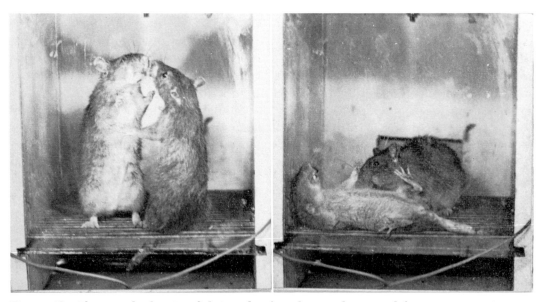

Figure 48. Photograph showing fighting chamber that we have used for many years in stress experiment on wild Norway rats.

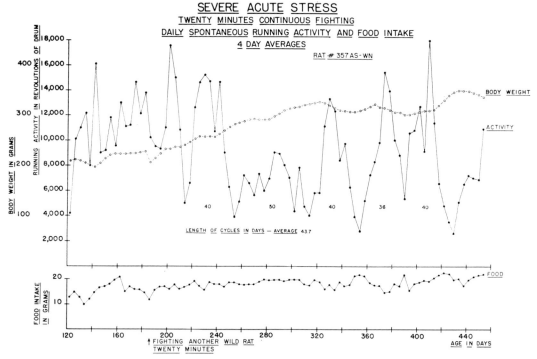

Figure 49. Graph showing long cycles of total daily spontaneous running activity and food intake (5 day averages) of a wild rat that had been fought with another wild rat for twenty minutes.

produced by fighting rats in a chamber shown in Figure 48, consisting of three wooden walls, a glass front and a floor made of iron rods, spaced three-fourths inches apart, and alternately wired to the opposite poles of an induction coil.[47] A single shock usually suffices to start two wild rats fighting. They often will fight to a state of complete exhaustion or even the death of one. A period of this very severe stress lasting only twenty to sixty minutes may leave effects from which the rats never recover. Figure 49 shows that a twenty minute period of fighting elicited regular long cycles that persisted throughout the rest of the animal's life. Likewise, forced swimming of forty-seven hours and fifty minutes re-

sulted in cyclic changes which persisted throughout the animal's life. Figure 50 shows the record of one such wild rat.

A male rat treated on one occasion with 120 microcuries of I[131] showed two long cycles of forty-five and forty days in length respectively.

A posterior lobectomized male rat showed three cycles of activity—sixty-five, fifty-five and fifty-five days in length. See Figure 51. Cyclic changes were not detectable in food intake.

Again we have no idea about the location of the forty to sixty day clock; nor do we know that all of these instances reported are significant of the existence of the same clock.

SEVENTY-SIX TO ONE HUNDRED AND

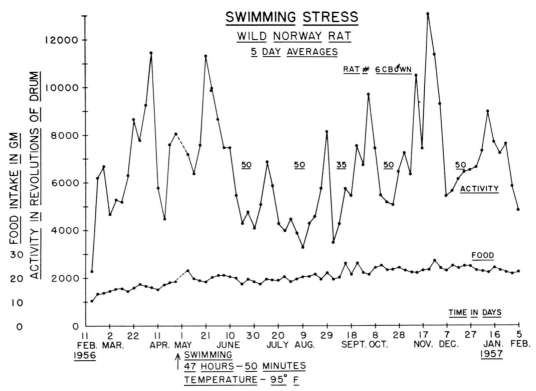

Figure 50. Graph showing long cycles of total daily spontaneous running activity (5 day averages) of a wild rat that had been forced to swim for forty-seven hours and fifty minutes.

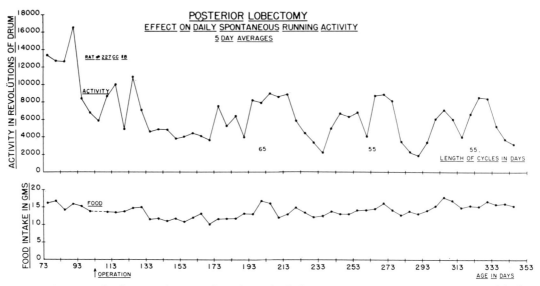

Figure 51. Graph showing long cycles of total daily spontaneous running activity (5 day averages) and food intake of a posterior lobectomized male rat.

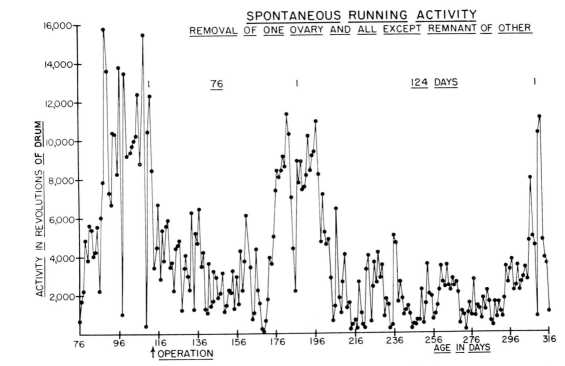

Figure 52. Graph showing seventy-six and 124 day cycles of total daily spontaneous running activity of a female rat from which one ovary and all except a small remnant of the other had been removed.

TWENTY-FOUR DAY CLOCK. In continuation of experiments carried out by Wang and Guttmacher[48] I removed one ovary and all except small remnants of the other in a number of domesticated rats. Some of these rats showed long swings of activity. Figure 52 shows the record of one such animal with two cycles of seventy-six and 124 days in length respectively.

It is possible that these cycles resulted from successive rupturing of large cysts that formed over the small remaining fragment of ovarian tissue.

ONE HUNDRED AND SIXTY TO ONE HUNDRED AND EIGHTY DAY CLOCK. This last appeared in one of our vagotomized rats. See Figure 53. Its activity showed two clear-cut cycles of 160 and 180 days in length respectively. We have no idea about the underlying mechanism of these cycles; in particular we have no idea why some vagotomized rats had cycles as short as twenty days in length, others 160-180 days, as was true of this rat.

C. Clocks found in Desert Rats, Pocket Mice, Ground Squirrels

Desert Rats

Daily records of activity, food and water intake have been taken on forty-eight desert rats at various times during the past thirty-four years.

THIRTY TO FORTY-FIVE DAY CLOCK. A few of these desert rats normally showed

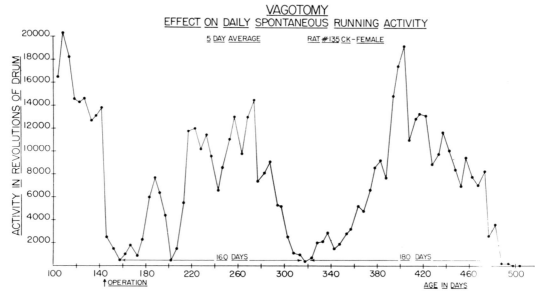

Figure 53. Graph showing 160 and 180 day cycles (5 day averages) of a vagotomized female rat.

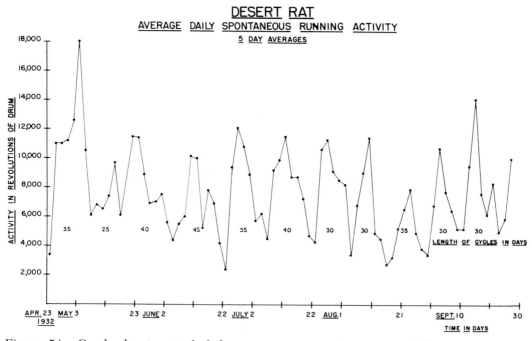

Figure 54. Graph showing total daily spontaneous running activity (5 day averages) of a normal desert rat.

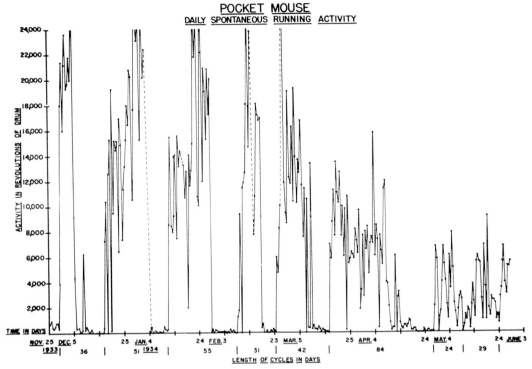

Figure 55. Graph showing total daily spontaneous running activity of a normal pocket mouse.

cycles that closely resembled some of those found in Norway rats after various forms of experimental interference. Cycles extraordinarily regular in their amplitude of swing, and averaging thirty-four days in length are shown in the record in Figure 54.

Pocket Mice

Records were taken on 6 pocket mice for many months. Most of them showed marked fluctuations in spontaneous activity, ranging from periods of eleven to twenty-five days of practically total inactivity to shorter periods at very high levels of 30,000 revolutions per day. Figure 55 shows a record of one of these animals. The total lengths of the cycles ranged from twenty-four to eighty-four

days. It is possible that the eighty-four day cycles represented two or more shorter cycles.

Blinded Ground Squirrels

Daily records were taken on fifty ground squirrels over periods of months and years at various times since 1930.

SEVEN TO THIRTEEN DAY CLOCK. A few blinded ground squirels, male and female, showed cycles of activity in the range of seven to thirteen days. Figure 56 shows the record of one of these animals, a male ground squirrel.

FOURTEEN TO FIFTEEN DAY CLOCK. A few blinded female ground squirrels showed fourteen to fifteen day cycles that closely resembled pseudopregnancy cycles of pituitary stalk sectioned Nor-

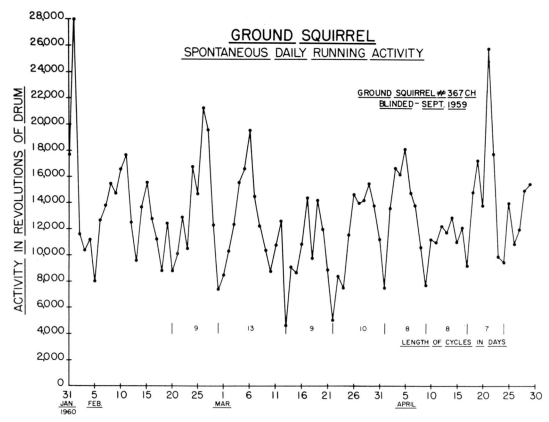

Figure 56. Graph of total daily spontaneous running activity of a normal male ground squirrel showing seven to thirteen day cycles of activity.

way rats. Figure 57 shows the record of a blinded ground squirrel that suddenly without having been subjected to any additional form of interference became almost totally inactive and showed what probably were clear-cut pseudopregnancy cycles.

THREE HUNDRED AND SIXTY-FIVE—OR NEARLY THREE HUNDRED AND SIXTY-FIVE—DAY CLOCK. Daily records of activity, food and water intake have now been taken on seven ground squirrels over 600 days. It would appear from our records that, freed from the influence of light, blinded ground squirrels no longer show yearly cycles of activity, but cycles

that are definitely shorter than 365 days and which may occur at any time of the year. They thus appear to become free-running cycles the same way that we saw the twenty-four—or nearly twenty four—hour cycles of the blinded rat become free-running. The activity record in Figure 58 of one of these blinded ground squirrels shows two clear-cut peaks, one in February, the other 270 days later with a peak in November.

D. Clocks found in Normal Man

Functioning clocks found in normal man are listed in the first column of Part II of Table I.

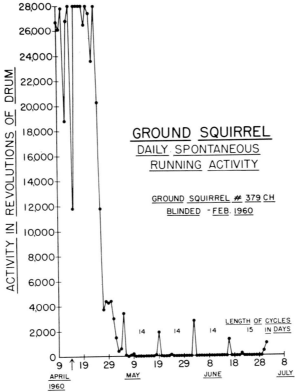

Figure 57. Graph of total daily spontaneous running
activity of a blind ground squirrel that showed
fourteen to fifteen day single day bursts.

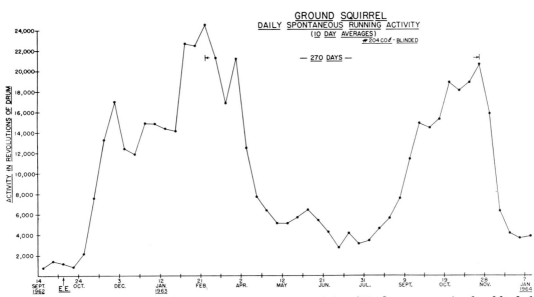

Figure 58. Graph of total daily spontaneous running activity (10 day averages) of a blinded
ground squirrel showing one 270 day cycle.

ONE AND ONE-HALF TO TWO HOUR CLOCK. The first clock met with in normal man measures time in units of one and one-half to two hours. It is the same clock which we saw in normal rats. It also manifests itself in spontaneous gross bodily activity.

Much of our information about this clock came from observations made in my laboratory many years ago by Dr. Tomi Wada, at that time a graduate student from Japan, and published in her doctor's thesis.[49] Because of the difficulty of obtaining records of spontaneous activity of human beings while they are walking, working, etc. Dr.

Wada decided to keep her subjects in bed and simply to record changes of position during waking and sleeping. A single tambour placed under the center of the bed and attached to a Marey tambour writing on a smoked drum gave adequate records. See Dr. Wada's drawing in Figure 59.

Dr. Wada found that both in the waking state and during sleep, adult subjects showed periods of activity every one and one-half to two hours; and that infants showed equally regular but more frequent periods of activity. In the record of a ten month old infant in Figure 60 taken during continuous sleep,

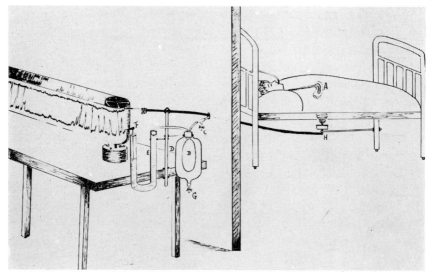

Figure 59. Drawing showing set-up for recording gross bodily movements in bed and stomach contractions. Wada.[49]

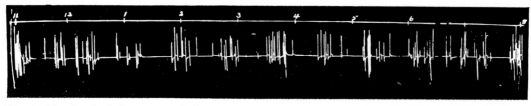

Figure 60. Smoked drum record showing period of gross bodily movements of a ten month old infant during nine hours continuous sleep in a crib. Time in hours. Wada.[49]

the periods of activity recurred at intervals of forty-five minutes on the average.

In her study on human subjects who learned to swallow a stomach tube with an attached balloon, Dr. Wada was actually able to establish a close relationship between periods of gross bodily activity and the stomach contractions—whereas in my study on rats I was only able to postulate such a relationship.

Dr. Wada's drawing in Figure 59 also shows the apparatus used in recording stomach contractions. Changes in pressure of an inflated balloon in the stomach were recorded on a smoked paper, along with gross bodily movements of the subject in bed. The record in Figure 61 demonstrates the relationship between periods of restlessness and stomach contractions during uninterrupted sleep. The top line shows time in half hour periods; the second line movements in bed; the third line stomach contractions. This record shows only two of the total of nine hours of uninterrupted sleep. It shows the end of one contraction period, followed by a quiescent interval, and another contraction period. During the contraction periods the subject showed marked restlessness, whereas during the quiescent periods he did not stir. This is typical of many records obtained by Dr. Wada.

The periodicity of this clock which manifests itself in periods of gross bodily activity and stomach contractions may vary through a wide range depending on the habits of the individual—times of meals, amounts of food eaten and fluids imbibed, times of going to sleep and awakening, etc. Whereas in some persons this clock is not very reliable, in others it may display a high degree of regularity, as we were able to observe in several subjects in 1921. For example, a medical student who served as subject during the spring quarter for many combined activity and stomach contraction records during sleep, was used for further observations in the fall immediately after his return from a summer spent working on a farm. For the two summer months on the farm his habits had been very regular—he went to bed at 10 P.M. and got up every morning at exactly 5 A.M. The sleep record showed that during the night he had three stomach contraction periods—during the first two of which he became restless but did not awaken, but that during the third he became progressively more restless and awakened very suddenly at the onset of the very large tetanic contractions that

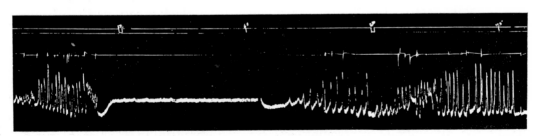

Figure 61. Smoked drum record showing stomach contractions and body movements during continuous sleep in bed. Time in half hours (Wada[49]).

occurred near the end of the period. These tetanic contractions started at 5 A.M. Here the stomach contractions definitely served as an alarm clock. Similar observations were made on this subject and on several others.

In the same way, in a person with regular eating and sleeping habits, stomach contraction periods (onset of tetanic contractions) may serve not only as an alarm clock in the morning for awakening, but also because of the close relationship to the sensation of hunger as an alarm for mealtimes during the day.

As has recently been demonstrated by Dement and Kleitman[50] this one and one-half to two hour clock apparently manifests itself during sleep not only in periods of gross bodily activity but also in eye movements and other functions.

Thus, we see that rats and man possess much the same type of one and one-half to two hour clock. The site of this clock still has not been determined. It is likely, however, that it depends on mechanisms in the brain as well as in the stomach.

TWENTY-FOUR HOUR CLOCK. Evidence for the existence of this clock in normal man is not very definite. Certainly normal man does not give evidence of possessing a clock that in any way resembles that of the rat with its one sharp onset of activity every twenty-four hours and its one sharp termination of activity twelve hours later. We do know that man may show small changes in body temperature and in other physiological functions, but the actuality of even these small changes come into doubt in view of: 1) the difficulty of controlling external conditions in man—habits of eating, sleeping, working, etc.; and 2) of

controlling internal periodic phenomena—particularly the stomach contractions and other periodic phenomena such, for instance, as distention of the bladder.

The chief evidence that has been offered at present for existence of a twenty-four hour clock in man is reported discomfort experienced by air travelers who lose or gain six to seven hours in a few hour's travel time. Many travelers, however, do not experience any such discomfort.

To obtain more definite information about the twenty-four-hour clock in man it will be necessary to take records of various functions of individuals maintained under rigidly controlled constant conditions, in bed, for several twenty-four-hour periods. To my knowledge no such records exist at the present time. The subjects would also have to be starved to eliminate all influences of digestive changes: results of our animal experiments demonstrated that starvation over a three to four day period has no effect whatsoever on the twenty-four-hour clock.

There certainly does not appear to be any evidence for the possession by normal man of a chronometer that can be consulted at any hour of the day.

TWENTY - EIGHT - DAY CLOCK. The menstrual clock measures time in units of twenty-eight days with great regularity in many women; with much less regularity in others. It manifests itself also in other functions, such for instance as body temperature, as may be seen in Figure 62. Here body temperature ranged from 97.0 to 98.5° at intervals of twenty-seven to thirty-one days, gradually increasing right up to the beginning

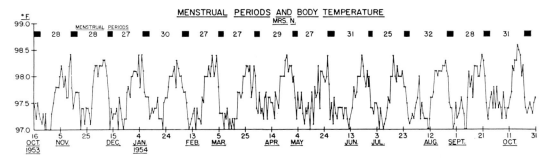

Figure 62. Chart showing cyclic changes in body temperature with relation to menstrual periods in a thirty-five year old normal woman. (Courtesy of Dr. Georgeanna Seager Jones.)

of menstruation, then falling off very sharply.

The location of this clock, whether in the ovaries, hypophysis, hypothalamus, or in all three, has not been established.

280-DAY CLOCK. This clock which measures the duration of pregnancy, is probably the most reliable of the few clocks that still make their appearance in normal human beings. The location of this clock likewise is not definitely known. No exhibit is needed for this well-known clock.

E. Clocks found in Patients with Various Periodic Somatic Illnesses

TWELVE-HOUR CLOCK. Evidence for the existence of a twelve-hour clock has been found in a number of patients. The record at the left in Figure 63 belongs to a nineteen year old girl whose body temperature was taken at frequent intervals throughout the day and night.[51] It shows regularly recurring peaks of body temperature (40.1-40.7°C) at twelve hour intervals, which had been present presumably continuously since

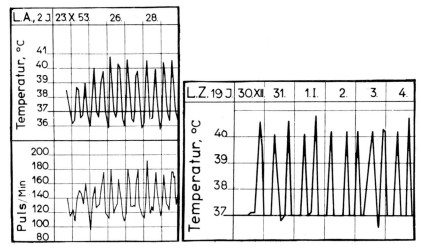

Figure 63. Graph showing 12 hour peaks of body temperature and pulse rate of a two year old girl (L.A.) and of body temperature of her mother (L.Z.) at age of 19 (Hitzig[51]).

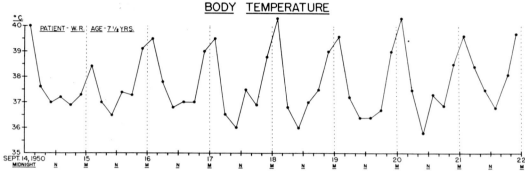

Figure 64. Record of body temperature of a seven and one-half year old boy who now after thirteen years still shows twenty-four hour peaks of body temperature shortly after midnight.

the age of nine months. At twenty-eight this woman gave birth to a daughter who at the age of five months also gave evidence of possessing a twelve-hour clock. At the right in Figure 63 are recorded the body temperatures and pulse records of the daughter at two years of age. Here we see twelve-hour peaks of the same regularity as those seen in the mother's record. This twelve-hour cycle was not present continuously but recurred at five month intervals each time for about fourteen days. During the fourteen days mother and daughter suffered from excessive sweating, stiff neck, neutrophilia, lymphopenia and occasional vomiting. They showed pathological encephalograms, but no signs of bacterial or parasitic infection. Mother and child were healthy in the intervals. Etiology of the fever remained unknown.

Twenty-four-Hour Clock. Evidence for the existence of a twenty-four-hour clock may be seen in the record in Figure 64 of body temperature of a boy who was first admitted to the Johns Hopkins Hospital at the age of seven and one-half years, for the diagnosis of unexplained fever. Body temperature fluctuated from 36-40°C reaching a peak every twenty-four hours just after midnight, even when the patient was kept in bed for long periods. This patient, now twenty-one years old, still shows this striking twenty-four hour cycle.

Figure 65 shows the body temperature record of a forty-three year old man in whom the twenty-four-hour clock manifested itself by sharp drops rather than increases in body temperature.[52] This patient suffered from diurnal attacks of chills and weakness for three months each year. About one hour after awakening in the morning he became literally drenched with sweat; his temperature dropped to between 93 and 96.4°F; within one to two hours he experienced a chill lasting about one hour; then within two to three hours his temperature increased to 98°F. He had these annual spells of chills for six years.

Forty-Eight-Hour Clock. This is one of the most remarkable of all clocks. It may manifest itself by sharp twenty-four-hour changes in function of almost every organ of the body. Hitzig[51] showed that in an eight year old boy with unexplained fever whose record is shown in Figure 66, this clock re-

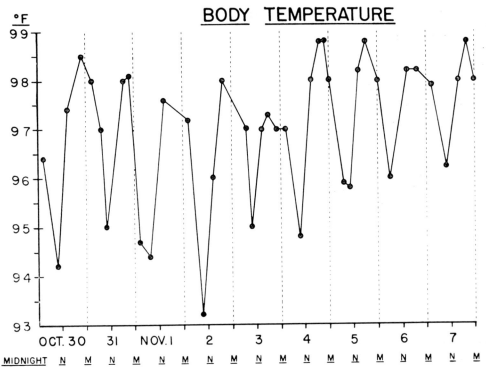

Figure 65. Record of forty-three year old man showing sharp decreases rather than increases in body temperature every twenty-four hours. Hoffman and Probirs.[52]

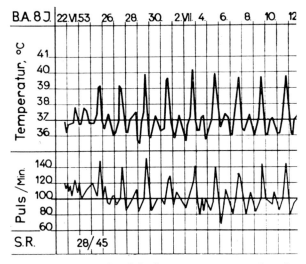

Figure 66. Graph of body temperature and pulse rate showing forty-eight hour peaks of eight year old boy (Hitzig[51]).

vealed its presence not only by changes in body temperature and pulse rate, but also by headaches, tremors in chin and legs, leucocytosis, and marked diuresis. His first episode at the age of four months consisted of a period of high fever, following small-pox vaccination. Between attacks the patient played and was free of all disturbances. From an enlargement of the third ventricle, polyuria and other symptoms, Hitzig concluded that the patient probably suffered from a lesion of the hypothalamus.

SEVEN-DAY CLOCK. The existence of a seven-day clock was demonstrated by Baker[53] in a forty-three year old engineer suffering form intermittent hydrarthrosis. Baker made daily measurements of the circumferences of the right and left knees. The record in Figure 67 shows

that the knees reached a maximum circumference every seven days. In each attack the knees remained swollen for three to five days; in the intervals the knees were normal. Greatly increased amounts of fluid in the synovial spaces produced the swelling. Of special interest, as will presently be seen, is the observation that the right knee reached its maximum usually three to four days after the left knee. The presence of Brucellosis in this patient was not a determining factor since the seven-day cycle persisted after the cure of the Brucellosis. Many patients with intermittent hydrarthrosis of the knee and elbow joints are on record. These patients often experience a sudden rush of fluid into the joints at the start of an attack.

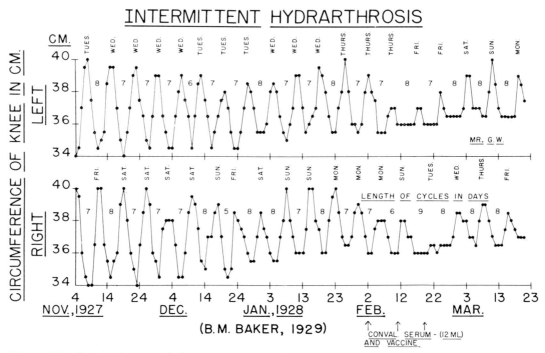

Figure 67. Graph showing daily measurements of the circumference of the right and left knee of a patient with intermittent hydrarthrosis (redrawn from Baker[53]).

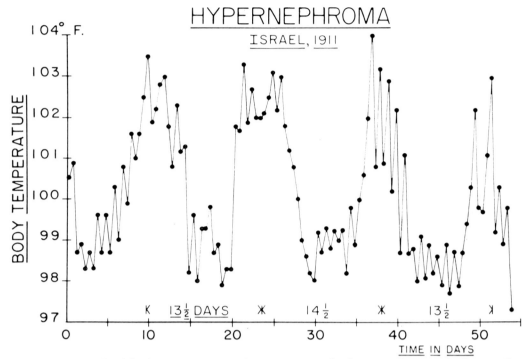

Figure 68. Record of body temperature of a patient with hypernephroma (redrawn from Israel[54]).

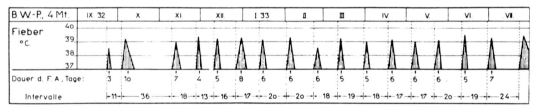

Figure 69. Record of body temperature showing seventeen to nineteen day peaks in a four month old boy (Hitzig and Fanconi[55]).

FOURTEEN-DAY CLOCK. A fourteen-day clock was found in a thirty-four year old female with an adrenal tumor (hypernephroma), as may be seen in the record of body temperature in Figure 68. (Isreal)[54] After removal of the adrenal tumor the temperature returned to normal and the cyclic changes disappeared.

SEVENTEEN TO NINTEEN DAY CLOCK. Evidence for the existence of a clock that measures time in units of nineteen days on the average comes from the body temperature record of a three year old boy suffering from unexplained recurrent fever. From an age of four months this boy had shown peaks of body temperature every nineteen days lasting six days. He died after an intestinal operation for ileus as did a twin brother. (Hitzig and Fanconi)[55] See Figure 69.

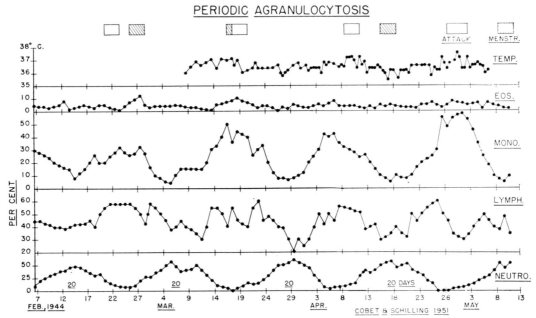

Figure 70. Record showing twenty to twenty-one day cycles in blood counts in patient with periodic agranulocytosis; also times of occurrence of attacks and menstrual periods (redrawn from Cobet and Schilling[56]).

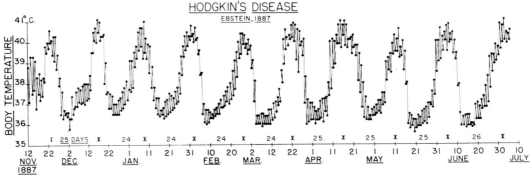

Figure 71. Record of body temperature of a patient with Hodgkins disease. Numbers over the base-line are lengths of temperature cycles (redrawn from Ebstein[57]).

TWENTY TO TWENTY-ONE DAY CLOCK. This is also a remarkable timing device. Its existence is clearly shown in the record of a patient with periodic agranulocytosis shown in Figure 70.[56] This chart shows daily records of body temperature, percentages of eosinophils, monocytes, lymphocytes and neutro-phils in the blood stream of a nineteen year old girl who was under close observation for over six years. The neutrophils decreased to zero every twenty to twenty-one days with great regularity for many years. Percentages of lymphocytes and monocytes (and eosinophils?) reached maxima on the days neutrophils dropped to zero, and dropped to lowest levels on the days that neutrophils reached their maxima. Body temperature showed no indication of the presence of this clock. Noteworthy is the complete independence of the menstrual and neutrophil cycles. Many such patients are on record as will be seen below.

TWENTY-FOUR OR TWENTY-FIVE DAY CLOCK. In the nineteen year old boy with Hodgkin's disease, whose 8 month's body temperature record is shown in Figure 71, a twenty-four to twenty-five day clock manifested itself in periodic enlargement of the spleen and in remarkable changes in body temperature.[57] This is the original record of Ebstein of the Pel-Ebstein syndrome (1887). Body temperature ranged from 35.8°C to over 41°C and the individual waves very closely resembled one an-

other, temperatures increasing each time at a gradual rate, and then falling precipitously to a lower level.

TWENTY-SIX TO THIRTY DAY CLOCK. This clock may manifest itself in either males or females in a variety of ways. The record in Figure 72 shows that in this sixty-one year old male this clock manifested itself by bleeding on the inner surfaces of the legs for four to eight days; and by a great decrease in blood platelets during each atttck.[58] This patient's periodic bleeding recurred at intervals of twenty-six to thirty days with regularity over a six year period.

FIFTY TO SIXTY DAY CLOCK. This clock manifested itself by unexplained attacks of acidosis in three children (2 boys and a girl). Figure 73 shows a record of one of these patients who was eight years of age at the time of her first attack.[59] The attacks were a few days in

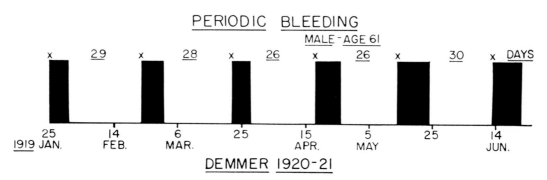

Figure 72. Record showing attacks of periodic bleeding in a sixty-one year old man (redrawn from Demmer[58]).

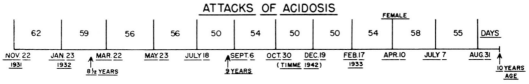

Figure 73. Record showing recurring attacks of acidosis in eight year old girl (redrawn from Timme[59]).

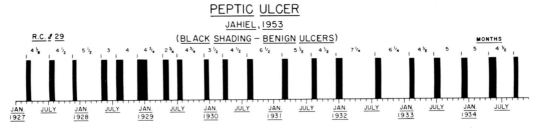

Figure 74. Eight year record showing periodic recurrence of attacks of peptic ulcer in a twenty-nine year old man (redrawn from Jahiel[60]).

length and lasted until her thirteenth year. From the age of one and one-half years she had suffered from a variety of endocrine and allergic illnesses. Later acidosis became the chief symptom which persisted up to her thirteenth year. Treatment with pituitary extract, thyroid powder and calcium lactate, helped to reduce the number and severity of attacks.

FOUR TO FIVE MONTH CLOCK. Evidence for the existence of this clock (Fig. 74) came from the record of a twenty-nine year old male who had recurrent attacks of peptic ulcers.[60] During the last ten to fifteen years the patient had suffered post-prandial pain in attacks which recurred with a fair de-

gree of regularity at an average of 140 days.

We have now come to the end of our exhibit of clocks that manifested themselves by changes in quite strictly limited somatic disturbances.

F. Clocks found in Patients with Various Forms of Periodic Mental and Emotional Illnesses

TWENTY-FOUR HOUR CLOCK. Observations made on psychiatric patients brought definite evidence for the existence of a twenty-four-hour clock in man. The record in Figure 75 is a good example.[61] This twenty-eight year old female with Parkinson's disease was completely incapacitated by marked

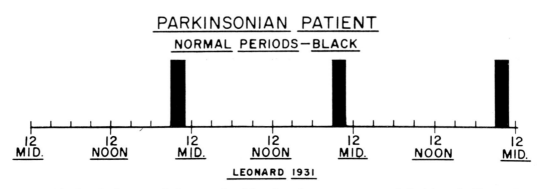

Figure 75. Graph showing daily periods of freedom from symptoms of Parkinson's disease in a twenty-eight year old female (redrawn from Leonard's clinical records[61]).

rigidity and tremors of legs and arms although alert mentally during the day and up to 9 P.M. in the evening; her hand-writing was indecipherable, her speech unclear. Each evening at 9 P.M. she suddenly became able to walk, talk, eat, drink, write and to take care of herself generally. This phase usually lasted two to three hours. These periodic changes were observed for years in the hospital. Her illness developed following an attack of lethargic encephalitis in early childhood.

According to Griffiths and Fox[62] who made a review of 39,920 fits in 110 males at the Litchfield Epileptic Colony in England, some epileptic patients have a daily fit at almost the same time every twenty-four hours, but each patient may have a fit at his own special time—which may be at any hour of the day or night. These authors state, however, that many of their patients tended to have their daily fits between 6 and 7 A.M.; or between 10 P.M. and midnight as may be seen in Figure 76. Langdon-Down and Brain reported similar diurnal variations in 66 institutionalized epileptics.[63]

FORTY-EIGHT-HOUR CLOCK. Evidence for the existence of this truly remarkable clock was seen in patients with strictly somatic illnesses, but it comes chiefly from observations made on patients with various forms of mental illnesses. There are now on record over a hundred patients in whom this clock was found. In most instances the patients may be very abnormal for twenty-four hours, then almost within minutes they become normal for twenty-four hours, and then after an equally sharp transition become abnormal. In one patient such cycles persisted for over thirty years.

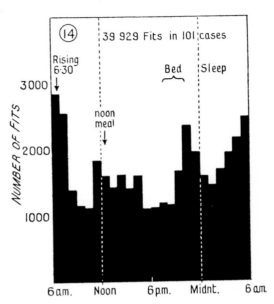

Figure 76. Bargraph showing twenty-four hour distribution of epileptic fits (Griffiths and Fox[62]).

When in 1925 records of four such patients at the Phipps Clinic were first brought to my attention I doubted their reality. Figure 77 shows part of the behavior chart of one such patient, a sixty-eight year old woman.[64] One day she was cheerful, spent time reading, etc., was normal in all her behavior, while on the next day she was very sad and fearful—actually suicidal. The chart also shows that on the normal days she slept quite well, while on abnormal days she slept little or not at all. The pulse rate did not clearly follow the cycle. It was not until 1935 that a chance finding of a report of two such patients by the Swiss psychiatrist, Eugen Bleuler,[65] encouraged me to publish records of our four patients. I did not learn until much later that Arndt in Germany had reported observations on eleven such patients in 1931.[66] Menninger - Lerchenthal, the

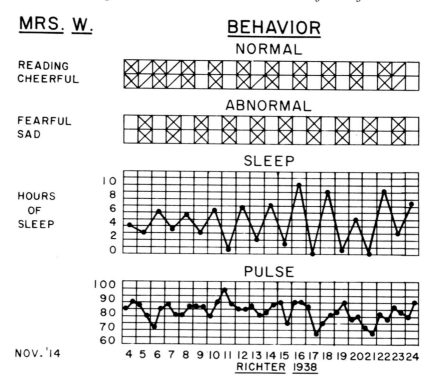

Figure 77. Part of behavior chart showing alternate twenty-four hour cycles of good and bad days in a manic-depressive sixty-eight year old woman.[64]

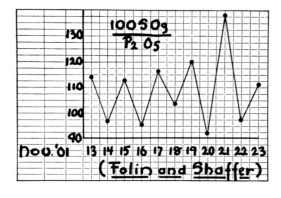

Figure 78. Graph showing changes of phosphorus metabolism in a psychiatric patient showing a forty-eight hour cycle of behavior and mood (redrawn from Folin and Shaffer[67]).

most active collector of these cases, found that one case had been reported as early as 1798.[5] The well-known biochemists, Folin and Shaffer (1902)[67] had made chemical studies on such a patient and had reported finding changes in phosphorus metabolism with relation to the cycles as may be seen in Figure 78. This forty-eight-hour clock has been found in all types of psychiatric patients: manics, depressives, schizophrenics, neurasthenics and hysterics.

FIVE-DAY CLOCK. A five-day clock has manifested itself in a variety of changes in behavior, but chiefly in hours

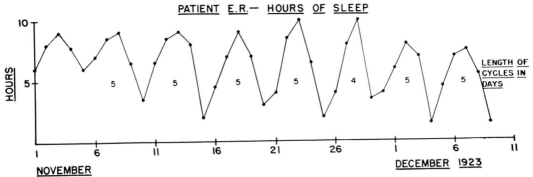

Figure 79. Graph showing a five day cycle in hours of sleep of a thirty year old woman in the Phipps Clinic (Richter[68]).

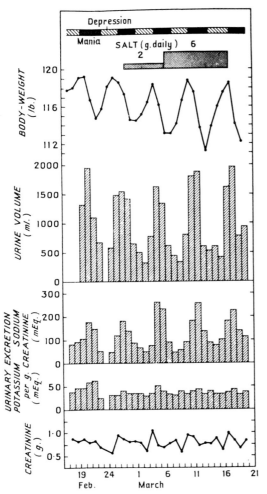

Figure 80. Record showing six day cycles in various physiological and behavioral functions in a manic-depressive patient (Crammer[69]).

of sleep, as may be seen in Figure 79.[68] This Phipps Clinic patient, a thirty year old woman, diagnosed as 'constitutional inferiority with hypomanic features,' was excited for three to four days and very sluggish for one to two days. Her hours of sleep clearly showed the presence of a five-day clock. Several such patients are on record.

SIX-DAY CLOCK. Evidence for the existence of this clock comes from observations on a number of patients—chiefly manic-depressives. Crammer[69] in England, made intensive biochemical and other studies on such patients, as may be seen in the record in Figure 80. Body weight, urine volume, and sodium excretion clearly revealed the presence of a six-day clock. Similar records have been reported by a number of other workers.

FOURTEEN-DAY CLOCK. Existence of a fourteen—or nearly fourteen—day clock was revealed by the occurrence of groups of fits in one of the epileptic patients observed by Griffiths and Fox as may be seen in Figure 81. #13.[62] This chart shows the times of occurrence and numbers of fits.

TWENTY-ONE-DAY CLOCK. Evidence of the existence of a twenty-one-day

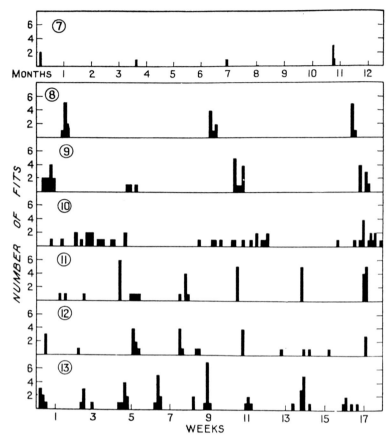

Figure 81. Record showing temporal distribution of fits for seven
epileptic patients (Griffiths and Fox[62]).

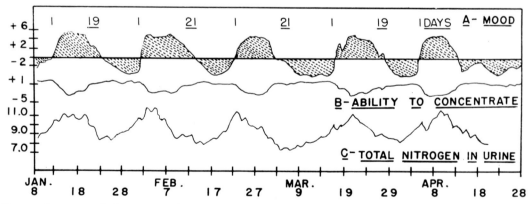

Figure 82. Record showing cycles in: A) mood; B) ability to concentrate; C) total nitrogen in
urine of a catatonic-schizophrenic patient (redrawn from Gjessing[4-III]).

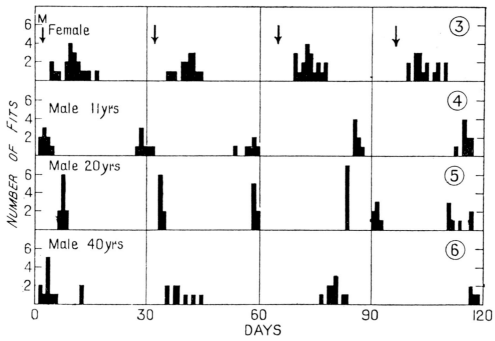

Figure 83. Record showing monthly cycles of occurrences of attacks in a female and three male epileptics. Abscissas time in days; ordinates number of fits (Griffiths and Fox[62]).

clock was likewise revealed in one of the epileptic patients observed by Griffiths and Fox, as may be seen in Figure 81. #11.[62]

Existence of a twenty-one-day clock was further demonstrated in a catatonic-schizophrenic patient studied by the late Norwegian biochemist and psychiatrist, Gjessing.[4-III] Part of the record of this patient in Figure 82 shows that periods of excitement alternated with periods of slightly depressed mood at intervals of nineteen to twenty-one days, and a sharp transition separated the two phases; the presence of the clock was also revealed in records on the ability to concentrate and total nitrogen excretions.

THIRTY-DAY CLOCK. The existence of a thirty-day clock was revealed in pa-

tients by changes in quite unrelated functions: in four patients—three males and one female—by the appearance for a few days every month of groups of epileptic attacks as may be seen in the record in Figure 83;[62] or by attacks of schizophrenic behavior lasting about ten days every thirty to thirty-one days, and by corresponding marked changes in urine output, in body temperature and pulse rate[70] (see Fig. 84); or by attacks of catatonic stupor every thirty—or nearly thirty—days, as may be seen in "G" of Figure 85.[71]

This last record is of particular interest since by replotting it in the manner of the record of the rat in Figure 16 it can be seen that a thirty-day clock became freed from some outside control, just as the twenty-four-hour clock of the

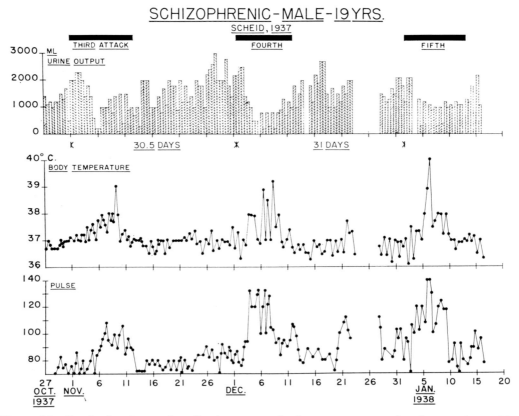

Figure 84. Graph showing cycles of urine output, body temperature and pulse rate in a schizophrenic patient showing periodic attacks at intervals of thirty to thirty-one days (redrawn from Scheid[70]).

rat becomes freed by removing control by light through blinding. In this patient for three years the clock ran faster, that is the onsets of stupor came earlier each month, as may be seen in "A," "B" and "C"; and then for three years the clock ran slower as seen in "D," "E" and "F"; that is, the onsets of stupor came later each month. We have no idea what entraining factor had been removed.

FORTY-DAY CLOCK. One of our Phipps Clinic patients, a fifty-six-year old school teacher manifested a forty-day clock as may be seen in the behavior chart, Figure 86. Markings for normal behavior are shown above the dividing line, for depressed behavior below the line.[72] On admission this patient complained of muscular cramps, restlessness, depression, diarrhea. For twenty days she was quiet, slow, and very much depressed; then, literally over night, her spirits became normal, she was active, took care of herself and had a good appetite. After another twenty days, equally suddenly, she became depressed again. She had been exposed to ammonia fumes during an explosion and subsequently had shown signs of parathyroid deficiency.

CATATONIC STUPOR

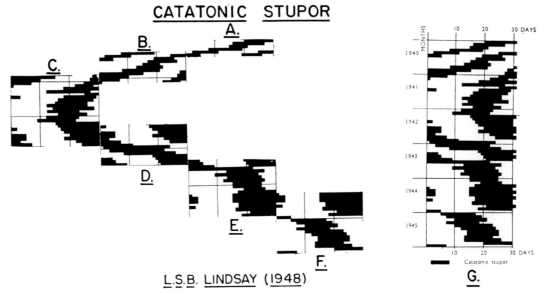

L.S.B. LINDSAY (1948)

Figure 85. Graph showing six year record of periods of stupor in a catatonic patient. (Lindsay's[71] original chart at right "G"; our version of chart "A," "B," "C," "D," "E," "F").

BEHAVIOR CHART

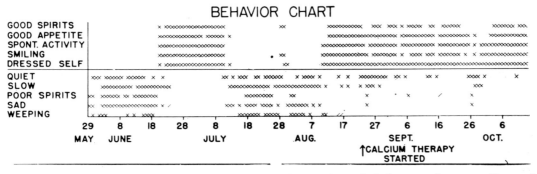

Figure 86. Part of a behavior chart of patient with parathyroid deficiency showing effects of treatment with calcium lactate solution and A.T. 10 (Dihydrotachysterol).[72]

Calcium therapy—free access to a 2.5 per cent solution of calcium lactate and administration of A. T. 10 (Dihydrotachysterol) abolished the cycles and restored the patient to good health. One of Griffiths and Fox's epileptics had a series of fits every thirty-eight days on the average, Figure 81, #9.[62]

The record of one of Gjessing's catatonic-schizophrenics with periodic stupor is of special interest because of its close similarity in lengths and characteristics of phases to those found in records obtained from thyroid deficient rats; especially since in both patient and thyroid deficient rats thyroid therapy abolished the cycles. Figure 87 shows two full cycles of Gjessing's patient.[4-II] The top graph shows estimation of the psychic state—stupor in degrees below the

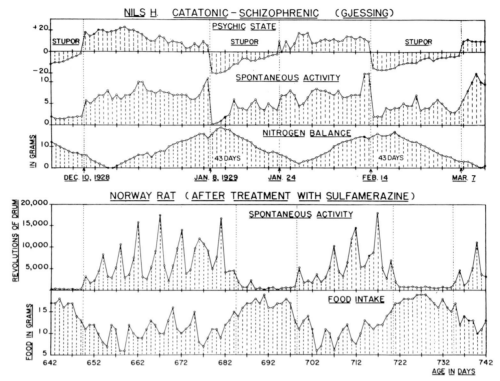

Figure 87. Top three graphs showing daily estimates of psychic state, spontaneous activity (in bed), and nitrogen balance respectively for catatonic-schizophrenic (redrawn from Gjessing[4-II]). Bottom two graphs showing daily spontaneous activity and amount of food intake respectively for rat whose thyroid had been damaged by sulfamerazine.

line; degrees of normal states above the line. The middle graph shows amounts of spontaneous activity in bed as determined by an actograph (the patient was kept in bed under constant conditions throughout the observations). These two graphs show a close correlation. They both show very sharp transitions between normal and abnormal phases—shifts from stupor to normal and vice-versa occurring literally over night. In marked contrast the third graph—nitrogen balance—shows very smooth sinusoidal curves—forty-three days in length. Below the record for the Norway rat belongs to an animal that for over 100 days

had been treated with sulfamerazine and which after cessation of treatment had developed very regular cyclical changes in spontaneous activity and food intake.[41] The top graph shows the regular alternation of active and inactive phases—the lengths of which are not very different from the two phases of the patient; likewise transition between phases was quite sharp. The lower graph shows that daily food intake had much more of a sinusoidal character resembling that of the nitrogen balance of the patient—also in lengths of waves. Noteworthy is that thyroid therapy abolished the abnormal cycles in the

BEHAVIOR CHART

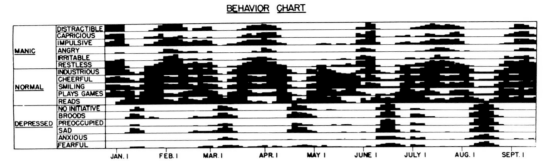

Figure 88. Part of behavior chart of fourteen year old manic-depressive boy showing daily markings of manic, normal and depressed mood (Rice[73]).

patient; thyroid treatment was not used in this rat, but was used in a number of other rats made thyroid deficient by sulfamerazine therapy, and it abolished the abnormal cycles.

FIFTY-TWO-DAY CLOCK. A fifty-two-day clock was found by Dr. K. K. Rice[73] in another Phipps Clinic patient, a fourteen year old boy whose behavior chart is shown in Figure 88. The markings on the chart show regular swings in behavior from manic, through normal, to depressed, to normal, to manic, etc. at intervals of fifty-two days on the average. These cycles persisted through an eight and one-half month stay in the Phipps Clinic and were still present after nine months in another hospital. Two epileptic patients experienced groups of fits on the average every fifty-two and fifty-six days respectively, Figure 81, #8 and #10.[62] This may be the same clock that was seen in the three children with periodic acidosis. See Figure 73.

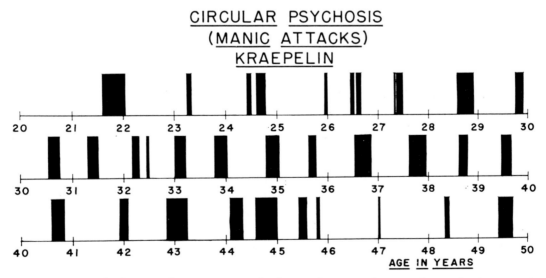

Figure 89. Graph showing thirty year record of annual, or nearly annual, attacks in a manic patient (redrawn from Kraepelin[74]).

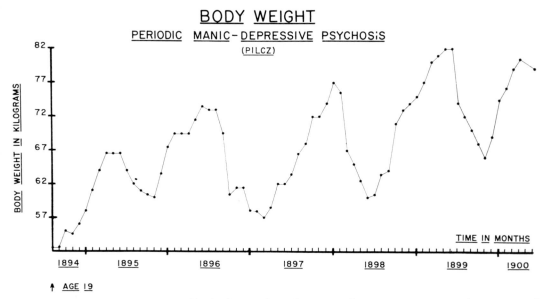

Figure 90. Graph showing monthly body weights of a manic-depressive patient in the Municipal
Hospital in Vienna over a six year period (redrawn from Pilcz[3]).

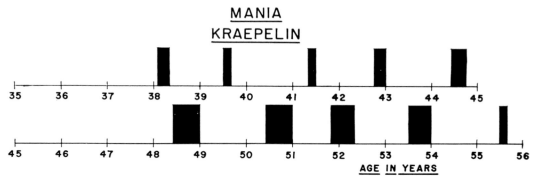

Figure 91. Graph showing two year cycles of attacks of a manic patient (redrawn from Kraepelin[74]).

ONE HUNDRED-DAY CLOCK. Evidence
for the existence of this clock came from
observations reported by Griffiths and
Fox on one of their epileptics, as may be
seen in Figure 81, #7.[62]

ONE-YEAR CLOCK. Clocks that measure time in units of one—or nearly
one—year have been found in many
psychiatric patients. Figure 89 shows a
record of one of these patients reported
by the German psychiatrist, Kraepelin.[74]
It shows that manic attacks were recorded in this patient at yearly—or
nearly yearly—intervals over a thirty
year period.

FIFTEEN-MONTH CLOCK. Records kept
of body weight of a nineteen year old
manic-depressive girl over a six year
period in the Municipal Hospital in
Vienna revealed the presence of a clock

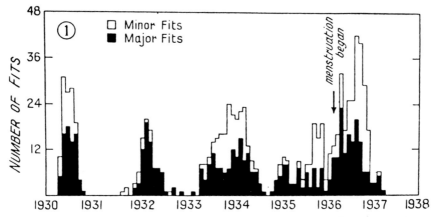

Figure 92. Graph showing two year cycles of occurrence of fits in an epileptic girl. The appearance of menstruation in 1936 upset the rhythm somewhat (Griffiths and Fox[62]).

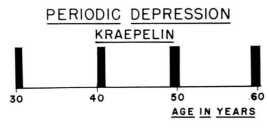

Figure 93. Graph showing ten year cycles in attacks of a depressed patient (redrawn from Kraepelin[74]).

that kept time in units of fifteen months on the average,[3] as may be seen in Figure 90. The weight variations were obviously unrelated to seasonal conditions since the maximum and minimum weights occurred without any relation to them.

TWO-YEAR CLOCK. The next clock kept time in units of two—or nearly two—years. Kraepelin[74] Its presence was revealed by attacks of mania, as may be seen in Figure 91. The existence of a two-year clock was revealed also in the record in Figure 92 of epileptic attacks of a patient who was observed over a seven year period by Griffiths and Fox.[62] Maximum of numbers of attacks occurred at quite regular intervals of two years.

TEN-YEAR CLOCK. Kraepelin[74] also reported the history of a patient who suffered from attacks of depression at very regular intervals of ten years, as may be seen in Figure 93. Whether this observation actually demonstrates the existence of a ten-year clock we do not know, but any record reported by Kraepelin, who was a very careful observer, certainly is worth reporting.

General Summary of Our Knowledge of Biological Clocks

A. Comparison of Clocks of Rats and Man

WE HAVE NOW seen that rats and other rodents as well as human beings harbor a great variety of clocks—clocks that operate quite independently of external events and influences. In view of the marked differences between rats and man in life spans (3 as compared to 70 years), lengths of ovulation cycles (4 as compared to 28 days), and pregnancy periods (22 as compared to 280 days), it is somewhat surprising to learn that the (time) units of many of the different clocks of rats and man extend over much the same range. Fig. 87 illustrates the close temporal relationship that may exist between one of the cycles found in rats and man.

Furthermore, we saw that when compared to a normal rat, normal man manifests far fewer timing mechanisms. However, under various pathological conditions, man manifests many different timing devices, quite as many as the rat.

In general, timing mechanisms found in man under various pathological conditions are much the same in patients suffering from mental or emotional disturbances as in patients suffering from somatic illnesses. It is noteworthy that in all instances of patients suffering from periodic illnesses with primarily mental and emotional symptoms, definite evidence was also found of periodic somatic changes.

Timing devices appear with equal frequency in patients with somatic illnesses and in patients with mental or emotional illnesses regardless of sex or age.

Finally, it was seen that these timing devices do not in any way depend on the presence of infectious organisms.

B. Manifestation of Clocks

A review of our information about clocks shows that under pathological conditions in man, clocks may manifest themselves in periodic changes in almost every organ of the body, as may be seen in Table II; or in almost every mental or emotional symptom, as may be seen in Table III.

In rats clocks may manifest themselves in spontaneous gross bodily activity, food and water intake, appetite for certain mineral solutions, body weight and vaginal smears. Further research on the rat will undoubtedly reveal manifestations in many other organs and functions—for instance, body temperature, pulse rate, neutrophil count, pupil size, etc.

1) Non-specific Manifestations

We saw that many manifestations of clocks were non-specific for lengths of clock units. Thus, recurring peaks of body temperature appeared at many

TABLE II

ORGANS AFFECTED IN PERIODIC DISEASES; AND ASSOCIATED CLINICAL MANIFESTATIONS

Organs	Clinical Manifestations
Joints (synovial spaces)	Intermittent hydrarthrosis, pain
Bone Marrow	Cyclic neutropenia, agranulocytosis (ulcers), thrombocytopenia (bleeding), reticulocytopenia (anemia)
Lymph Glands	Cyclic lymphocytosis, monocytosis, fever, Hodgkin's disease
Stomach and Duodenum	Cyclic peptic ulcers, vomiting, diarrhea, fever
Peritoneum	Benign paroxysmal peritonitis, pain, fever
Salivary Glands	Cyclic excessive secretion
Sweat Glands	Cyclic excessive sweating
Spleen	Cyclic neutropenia, fever
Kidney	Cyclic hematuria, oliguria, polyuria, fever
Muscles	Familial periodic paralysis
Eyes	Cyclic iritis, polyserositis
Skin	Cyclic purpura, urticaria, angio-neurotic edema, erythema, fever
Brain	Cyclic epilepsy, hypo- and hyperthermia, insomnia, hypersomnia, headache, migraine

TABLE III

MENTAL AND EMOTIONAL STATES IN PERIODIC ILLNESSES

Elation	Hypo-or hypersomnia
Excitement	Bulimia
Mania	Dipsomania
Depression	Hypochondriasis
Paranoia	Hallucinations
Stupor	Actual changes of personality

different intervals—in one individual every twenty-four hours, another every seven days, in another every twenty-eight days, etc. This is clearly demonstrated in the distribution chart for 123 individuals in Figure 94 which shows the number of patients with relation to lengths of clock units from twelve hours to thirty-two days. Likewise, we saw that pulse rate, leucocytosis, epileptic seizures, purpura, pain, as well as mania, depression, excitement, stupor, were non-specific for lengths of clock units.

Of interest in Figure 94 are the high numbers of patients with cycles of seven, or multiples of seven, days in length.

In rats, running activity, food and water intake, also were non-specific for any lengths of clock units.

2) *Specific Manifestations*

Several instances were found in which manifestations are highly specific for definite lengths of clock units.

The first instance concerns periodic swelling of the joints in patients with intermittent hydrarthrosis. In these patients lengths of clock units fell between seven and fourteen days inclusive, as may be seen in the distribution chart for 128 patients in Figure 95. Swelling of joints did not occur as a manifestation of any other clock units.

The next instance of specific manifestations concerns periodic disappearance of neutrophils from the blood stream in patients with periodic agranu-

locytosis. Here again lengths of clock units were concentrated at twenty-one days with a small scattering above and below twenty-one days, as may be seen in the distribution chart in Figure 96 (*top*).

A third instance of such specificity concerns periodic swelling and recession of the lymph glands and presumably corresponding fluctuations in numbers of lymphocytes in the blood stream in patients with Pel-Ebstein type of Hodgkin's disease. Here again lengths of clock units as revealed by accompanying changes in body temperature fell within a narrow range—not, however, as narrow as that of the two previous clocks.

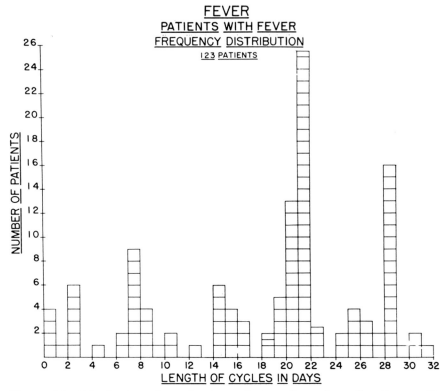

Figure 94. Distribution chart showing relation of number of patients with periodic fever to length of clock units.[1]

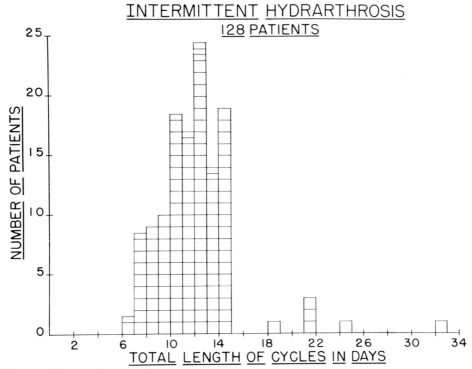

Figure 95. Distribution chart showing relation of number of patients with intermittent hydrarthrosis to length of clock units.[1]

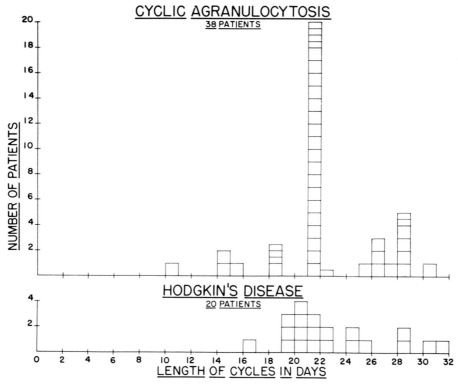

Figure 96. Distribution chart showing relation of number of patients with periodic agranulocytosis to lengths of clock units *(top)*; and same for patients with Pel-Ebstein syndrome of Hodgkin's disease *(bottom)*.

TABLE IV

CONDITIONS OR FORMS OF INTERFERENCE THAT MAY BRING OUT
PERIODIC PHENOMENA OF VARIOUS KINDS IN RATS

Greatly reduced thyroid activity—by surgery, treatment with I^{131} or anti-thyroid drugs

Removal of posterior lobe of pituitary gland; section of pituitary stalk

Brain lesions—particularly in tectum, pretectal region

Removal of parathyroid glands

Partial hepatectomy

Ligation of the bile duct

Removal of one ovary and all except remnants of other

Vagotomy

Starvation

Dehydration

Severe stress—forced swimming, fighting

One hour feedings over long periods

Brain tumors

Hypersensitivity

Dietary deficiencies

Vascular damage to vessels of brain

Prolonged treatment with various drugs and hormones

TABLE V

AGENTS THAT PRODUCED 10-14 DAY CYCLES DURING TREATMENT IN FEMALE RATS

Anti-biotic	*Hormones*
Sulfamerazine	Progesterone
	Prolactin
	Methyltestosterone

AGENTS THAT PRODUCED 10-14 DAY CYCLES AFTER THE TERMINATION OF TREATMENT
IN FEMALE RATS

Drugs

Anti-biotic	*Anti-thyroid*	*Anti-pyretic*	*Sedative*	*Others*
Sulfamerazine	Thiourea	Aminopyrine	Barbital	Gold Chloride
	Thiouracil	(Pyramidon)		Morphine Sulphate
	Propylthiouracil			

Hormones

Estradiol	Cortisone
Progesterone	Adrenalin

Vaccine

H. Pertussis

TABLE VI

CONDITIONS THAT MAY BRING OUT PERIODIC PHENOMENA IN MAN

Trauma	Vascular damage to brain
High fever	Brain tumor
Various illnesses	Brain lesions
lethargic encephalitis	Debilitation
cerebral arteriosclerosis	Thyroid deficiency
syphilis	Parathyroid deficiency
Severe stress—shock	Food and other allergies

Figure 96 (*bottom*) shows the distribution chart of clock units for twenty patients with this type of Hodgkin's disease.

Another possible instance may be mentioned—it concerns periodic bleeding from the skin and changes in number of platelets. Many individuals are on record who bled from the skin on various parts of the body with great regularity every seven days. We have a record, however, of one patient in whom bleeding from the skin occurred at twenty-six to thirty day intervals (see Fig. 72)—coinciding with a great decrease in blood platelets—so bleeding may be less specific than some of the three other manifestations cited.

C. Conditions Conducive to Their Appearance

Table IV lists the various conditions or forms of interference that brought out various kinds of periodic phenomena in rats: in some instances damage to endocrine glands; in others to the brain; in others to peripheral organs; in still others damage to the entire organism. Prolonged administration of a variety of drugs and hormones either during treatment or after cessation of treatment brought out the ten to fourteen day cycles in females. See Table V.

Table VI lists conditions that are known to be responsible for the manifestation of one or the other of various kinds of periodic phenomena in man. There probably are many more.

In patients suffering from periodic somatic or mental illnesses these clocks may manifest themselves spontaneously —in the absence of any disturbing stimuli; likewise they may disappear without out any detectable influences.

Some individuals undoubtedly are particularly susceptible to influences that allow clocks to manifest themselves. This is true of members of the same family in whom cycle-proneness may be inherited. Thus, the appearances of cyclic phenomena have been followed through five generations in one family.[75] Of interest here is the wide-spread distribution of periodic phenomena among Arabs, Jews and Armenians, in the form of Mediterranean disease, so-called because of its high incidence particularly of periodic abdominalgia, etc.[76] in this part of the world.

D. Characteristics of Clocks

These various biological clocks have the following characteristics:

1) *Accuracy*

Some of the clocks show a high degree of accuracy. This is true particularly of the twenty-four- or nearly twenty-four-hour clock of rats which in some instances tells time over periods of many months with only a few minutes error. Likewise, ovulation, pseudopregnancy, and pregnancy clocks of rats keep time with a high degree of accuracy. In man under pathological conditions the twenty-four-hour and particularly the forty-eight-hour clock also keep time with great accuracy. In some women the menstrual clock may keep very accurate time. In some patients with intermittent hydrathrosis or periodic agranulocytosis the clocks are so accurate as to provide accurate time. Many other illustrations of accuracy of these timing devices could be given.

2) *Constancy of Clocks*

In rats we saw that the pseudopregnancy clock once started—for instance by stalk section or posterior lobectomy, etc., keeps accurate time throughout the rest of the animal's life. The four to five day estrus clock of rats likewise keeps accurate time—usually for at least two years of the female's life.

In man, under pathological conditions, the forty-eight-hour clock of alternate good and bad days, etc., has been known to keep perfect time as long as thirty years.[77, 78] In one patient with intermittent hydrarthrosis the knees became swollen every thirteen days for over ten years; in a patient with cyclic agranulocytosis the neutrophils dropped to zero every twenty days for over eight years. Many other instances of great accuracy of various clocks in man are on record.

3) *Independence of External and Internal Events*

We saw that the various clocks show a high degree of independence of external and internal events. Thus, in a patient with intermittent hydrarthrosis, a thirteen-day clock continued to keep time with accuracy over years, in spite of all kinds of changes in weather and surrounding conditions, as well as of all kinds of internal changes. The independence of external or internal events was most clearly seen in the functioning of the twenty-four-hour clock in rats. We learned that in blinded rats this clock keeps perfect time in spite of almost every conceivable form of internal or external interference.

In experiments on the twenty-four-hour clock of rats we saw that this clock is regulated by light, but may function at its twenty-four- or nearly twenty-four-hour cycle entirely independently of light in blinded rats. In our experience light is the only factor that can regulate this twenty-four-hour clock in normal rats.

In man under pathological conditions, the twenty-four and forty-eight hour clocks are not regulated by light, since transition between the two phases may occur at any hour of the day or night. That, however, they are entrained by some other twenty-four hour factor is seen by the fact that transitions between phases occur at the same time each day or night with a high degree of accuracy. We know, however, that the forty-eight-hour clock may become freed from this unknown factor, since in one patient seen by Professor Eugen Bleuler, each phase was twenty-five hours in length rather than twenty-four;[65] and in another seen by Professor P. Näcke, one phase (excitement) had an average length of twenty-five hours and the other (stupor) twenty-nine hours.[78] Thus, in both instances over a period of months transitions between phases occurred at all times of the day and night.

We saw that in a catatonic-schizophrenic patient (see Fig. 85) a thirty-day cycle of stupors also apparently was freed from some external control—other than light—that allow the stupor to commence at an earlier time each month over a period of several years; then for a time at exactly thirty days; and finally later every month. Here this thirty-day clock appeared to be freed of its control in the same way, as in the rat, elimination of the entraining effects of light by blinding or constant darkness freed the twenty-four-hour clock. We have no idea what the controlling factor could have been in this case.

We saw a further instance in which elimination of light may have freed another cycle—the yearly cycle of activity in the ground squirrel allowing the yearly period of activity to come earlier each year after blinding.

E. Treatment of Rats and Patients Manifesting Clocks

With few specific exceptions, rats or patients manifesting abnormal periodic phenomena have resisted all forms of treatment. Administration of thyroid powder abolished the twelve to thirteen day inactive phases of thyroid deficient rats and restored them to their normal four or five day cycles, as may be seen in Figure 97. Likewise in periodic catatonic-schizophrenia, Gjessing,[4-I, II, III]

Stokes,[79] Gornall *et al.*,[80] Mall,[81] Lindsay,[82] and others have found that administration of thyroid powder or thyroxine will in many instances abolish the cycles of abnormally large swings of behavior. Figure 98 shows the effects of treatment with thyroxine and desiccated thyroid powder in a catatonic-schizophrenic who for years had experienced regularly recurring periods of excitement at intervals of forty to forty-five days.[80] Figure 86 shows the abolishment of forty-day cycles in mood and behavior in a patient with parathyroid deficiency by administration of A. T. 10 (Dihydrotachysterol) and by providing free access to a solution of calcium lactate.[72]

Various treatments have been used in many other patients but without success. Likewise we have tried without success all kinds of treatments in rats in which various cyclic phenomena have

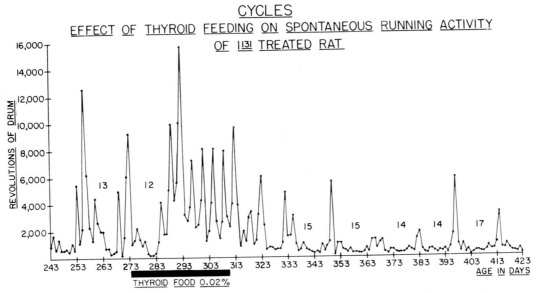

CYCLES
EFFECT OF THYROID FEEDING ON SPONTANEOUS RUNNING ACTIVITY OF I¹³¹ TREATED RAT

Figure 97. Graph showing effect of administration of thyroid powder on I[131] produced pseudo-pregnancy cycles.[38]

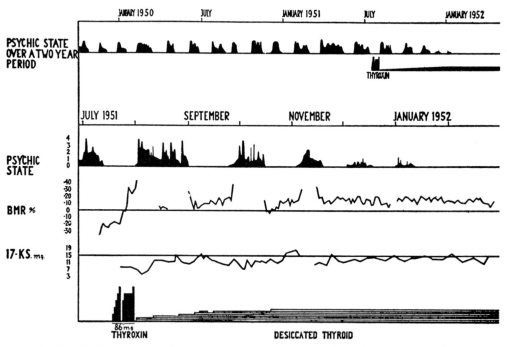

Figure 98. Graph showing periodic excitement in catatonic-schizophrenic and effect of treatment with thyroxine and dessicated thyroid powder (Gornall, Eglitis, Miller, Stokes and Dewan[80]).

been elicited by one form or another of experimental interference.

F. "Hands" of Clock

In rats we saw that spontaneous gross bodily activity—either in stationary cages or revolving drums—serves as a 'hand' for many clocks. It serves to disclose not only that the clock is functioning, but also at what rate. Since bodily activity is not part of the clock mechanism it follows that the clock can continue to function in the absence of activity. This fact was clearly demonstrated in the case of the twenty-four—or nearly twenty-four—hour clock of

rats treated with electro-shock or nitrous oxide gas, as well as of rats subjected to swimming, hypothermia, etc. See Figure 21. We saw that eating and drinking may also serve as "hands." Sleep and resting, however, do not serve as "hands" since they may occur at any hour of the day or night without any regularity.

In man most or all of the non-specific manifestations may serve as "hands" of the clock. The specific manifestations also tell us that the clock is running and at what rate, but they can not actually serve as "hands" since they do not have an existence apart from the clock. They might be thought of as "wheels" of the clock.

Three Kinds of Biological Clocks

IN REVIEWING all our data on periodic phenomena both for animals and man it occurred to me that the various clocks might be put into three groups:

    A. Homeostatic
    B. Central
    C. Peripheral

A. Homeostatic Clocks

In all of our early experiments on the production of cycles through various means of interfering with the functioning of the endocrine glands it seemed clear that we were dealing with homeostatic mechanisms—a feed-back operation between a target organ—an endocrine gland, the pituitary and various centers in the hypothalamus. The four or five day estrous cycle of the rat is a good example of such a clock; also the cycles produced by removal, surgical or chemical, of all except small remnants of the thyroid gland. Several diagrams illustrating this feed-back relationship were devised.[41] Early in our experiments it seemed that operation of all clocks could be understood as efforts of the organism to achieve homeostasis. Operation of a feed-back mechanism would tend to limit the accuracy of this kind of clock. As a matter of fact, the range of accuracy of one such clock, the menstrual clock of women, is quite wide —as may be seen in the distribution chart in Figure 99 which shows the distribution curve of the duration of 14,512 menstrual cycles in 1165 women;[83] or in Figure 100 which shows the frequency distribution of the duration of cycles of excitement or stupor in thirty-one catatonic-schizophrenic patients.

B. Central Clocks

However, as we became more familiar with the twenty-four—or nearly twenty-four—hour clock, and saw that it keeps perfect time independently of almost every internal or external change, it became clear that this clock could not be understood in terms of the operation of a homeostatic mechanism. Our evidence showed that this clock exerts an important control over many functions of the organism—but we found no evidence of a feed-back of any kind. We were forced to conclude then that the body harbors a second kind of timing device—central clocks. Apparently the site of this twenty-four—or nearly twenty-four—hour clock is in the hypothalamus, a position from which it can control many autonomic functions as well as total organism responses without involving any sort of feed-back mechanism. It appears that a number of such clocks may be harbored in different parts of the central nervous system.

The forty-eight-hour clock of patients with somatic and mental periodic illnesses is another example of this kind of clock, as are the eighteen and thirty-day clocks.

In contrast to homeostatic clocks, these central timing devices keep time

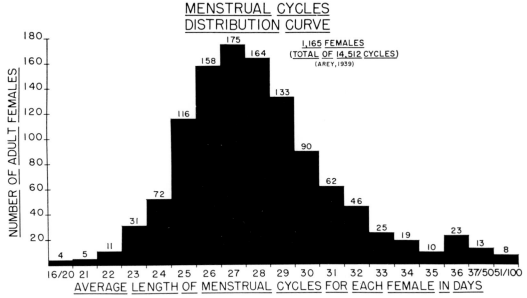

Figure 99. Distribution chart showing relation between number of cycles (1,165 women— 14,512 cycles) and lengths of menstrual cycles (Arey[83]).

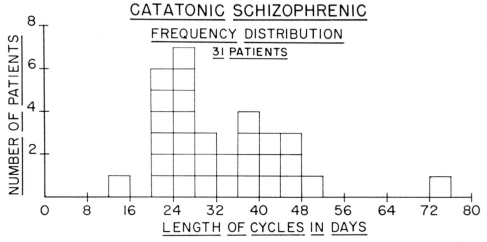

Figure 100. Distribution chart showing relation between numbers of catatonic-schizophrenic patients and lengths of cycles.[1]

with a high degree of accuracy and constancy over long periods.

The acceptance of the existence of central clocks means that body functions may be controlled not only by homeostatic but by non-homestatic mecha-

nisms—mechanisms that serve to maintain fixed time schedules rather than fixed physiological levels. Further, it seems likely that the central clocks are the more primitive since the presence of the twenty-four—or nearly twenty-four

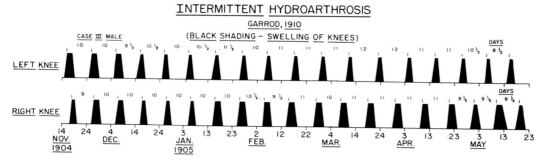

Figure 101. Graph showing the occurrence and duration of swelling of the right and left knees in a patient with intermittent hydrarthrosis (Garrod[84]).

—hour clock in unicellular and other lower organisms has been well established.

C. Peripheral Clocks

The study of histories of patients with intermittent hydrarthrosis and periodic agranulocytosis suggested that we are dealing with still a third kind of timing device—a peripheral clock, i.e., a clock located outside of the nervous system and quite independent of this system and of any homeostatic mechanisms. In some patients with intermittent hydrarthrosis several joints might show the same period—for instance seven days—but not be in phase—one joint, reaching a peak swelling on a Thursday, the other on Friday for example; while in others we saw that two joints not only might be out of phase but have different periods—as may be seen in Figure 101, which shows that swelling of the right knee reached a peak on the average every 10.0 days, that of the left knee every 10.6 days.[84] In still other patients the cycles of three or more affected joints have been reported to operate quite independently of one

another—and, most important, in all —or nearly all—of these cases, the periodic swelling occurred without any mental or nervous accompaniments. In other words, the joints have their own inherent rhythm—seven to fourteen days in length.

Periodic agranulocytosis is another example of this kind of clock—located in the neutrophil producing mechanisms in the bone marrow. Patients with periodic agranulocytosis show no mental or emotional changes except of a reactive type in a few instances—during the regularly recurring periods of neutropenia. Here we must assume an inherent rhythm of twenty-one days for the neutrophil-producing mechanisms.

Similarly the lymphocyte producing mechanism in the lymph glands of patients with the Pel-Ebstein syndrome of Hodgkin's disease appears to be another example of peripheral clock. It too functions quite independently of the central nervous system.

These peripheral clocks differ in location from the central clocks, but like them, tend to keep time with a high degree of accuracy and constancy.

Shock-phase Hypothesis

How DO THESE various clocks work? What do they have in common? How can we account for the fact that they may appear and disappear or operate for years without doing any detectable damage to the individual?

A. Hypothesis and Postulates

In thinking about these questions an idea presented itself which later took form as the 'shock-phase' hypothesis. This idea came partly from consideration of results of experiments carried on by Kalmus,[85] Pittendrigh and Bruce[86] on the fruit fly; and partly from the study of histories of many patients with all kinds of periodic illnesses, but particularly intermittent hydrarthrosis.

Kalmus, Pittendrigh and Bruce reported that in a colony of pupae of the common fruit fly, when exposed to twelve hours of light and twelve hours of darkness, the pupae emerge at twenty-four hour intervals—their inherent emergence rhythm—that is, they are in phase with one another; that, however, when the colony is kept in constant darkness, the flies emerge at all hours of the day and night, giving a constant emergence rate; that is, the individuals are all out-of-phase with one another. Also these workers reported that when a colony is kept in constant darkness, short exposure to light, even only a flash, may bring all pupae into phase so that they emerge at the same time at twenty-four hour intervals.

We might, in the same way, think of the secretory synovial membrane of a joint as being constituted of a colony of cells each one of which has the same inherent rhythm (of durations from 7 to 14 days); further that under normal conditions, the individual cells of a joint function phasically independent of one another, some being active, some inactive, others at various stages between—thus ensuring a fairly constant total secretory rate and the maintenance of constant size of the joint; that, however, after a shock or trauma, the cells may all suddenly be thrown into phase, all secreting at more or less the same time, and all stopping secreting at more or less the same time—thus giving rise to periodic fluctuations, or intermittent hydrarthrosis.

In the same way, according to this hypothesis, in normal individuals, neutrophil producing cells in bone marrow function out-of-phase, thus giving rise to a fairly constant number of neutrophils; however, a shock or trauma may throw these cells into the same phase, resulting in the appearance of a twenty-one-day rhythm in number of neutrophils—the inherent rhythm of the individual cells.

We may also assume that under normal conditions the lymphocyte-producing cells are functioning at different phases, giving rise to a fairly constant number of lymphocytes in the blood stream, but that after a shock or trauma they are all thrown into the same phase, giving rise to marked fluctuations at a period near twenty days. Likewise under normal conditions platelet-producing cells and bone marrow may all function out of phase, but after a shock of some kind may all be thrown into phase at or near seven days.

It seems possible that the lengths of the cycles of these patients might provide a measure of the life-span of neutrophils, lymphocytes and platelets. Of interest here is that on the basis of entirely different methods the life-span of neutrophils has been estimated to be near ten days;[87] of lymphoctes—twenty days;[88] of platelets six to ten days.[89]

We may consider the possibility that 120—or nearly 120—day cycles found in some patients may be associated with the 120-day life-span of red cells. Thus far, no one to my knowledge has made daily red-cell counts in any patients showing cycles of approximately this length.

Thus, the shock-phase hypothesis consists of the following postulates:

1) That each one of the functioning units of an organ or brain center—cells, follicles, etc. has an inherent rhythm, the length of which is characteristic of that organ or center.

2) That these units may operate in unison, in phase—that is they may all be active at one time, or inactive, or in various stages between; further, although physically closely bound together the units may operate quite independently of one another—out-of-phase—some being in a stage of inactivity, some at various stages between activity and inactivity.

3) That an organ or center whose units are functioning in phase has a rhythmic performance, the length of the rhythm corresponding to the inherent rhythm of the constituent units; that an organ or center whose units are functioning out-of-phase has an even—nonrhythmic performance.

4) That in their simplest, most primitive forms, organs and centers have a rhythmic function—that is, their constituent units are all in phase; that in the process of evolution the tendency is for units to function progessively more and more out of phase, thus giving rise to an even performance of the organs and centers—man being the chief representative of this state.

5) That in an organ or center in which the units are functioning out-of-phase, the units may temporarily or permanently all be thrown into phase by a severe shock, trauma, or other factors.

6) That under certain circumstances the synchronized units of an organ or center may be desynchronized by various forms of interferences—or spontaneously—thus restoring the organs or centers to their normal non-cyclic activity.

7) That the lengths of the rhythms of units may have been built into an organ or center by external cyclic changes—for instance the twenty-four-hour period of light and darkness; that the lengths of the rhythms may reflect metabolic conditions of the organ or center—the lengths of periods of activity and following periods of rest; that they may reflect the life-span of individual units.

B. Evidence for Hypothesis

The shock-phase hypothesis rests on the postulate that individual units of an organ may function quite independently of one another—that is, one may be active, while the adjoining component may be inactive, and still others in various degrees of activity.

We know from our observations and those of other workers that the follicles of the thyroid gland of a normal rat may be in all degrees of activity. Furthermore, from the observations of Williams[90] it is known that the follicles may show quite regular cyclic changes in activity and quite independently of one another.

Similarly, Bradford and Davis[91] found by means of special dyes that the cells of the gastric mucosa may at any one time be in all stages of activity. Professor D. Fawcett* at Harvard working with the electron microscope found that at any one instance even adjoining cells of the gastric mucosa can be in opposite states of activity.

Smith[92] reported that the glomeruli of the kidney may likewise function quite independently of one another.

According to Franck[93] the individual neurons of various centers of the brain may also operate independently of one another.

Strumwasser *et al.* have contributed the most interesting and pertinent evidence.[94] In one series of experiments in which he recorded brain temperatures of ground squirrels at various phases of hibernation, he found synchronized changes in the electro-encephalogram of the amygdala.

In another experiment[95] Strumwasser recorded potentials from a definitely

identical neuron in the parieto-visceral ganglion of *Aplysia californica*. The ganglion was isolated from all peripheral receptors and kept in sea water or in artificial media. He found that this neuron was active for eight hours of each twenty-four, starting each night at 1700-1900 hours and inactive for the rest of the twenty-four hours. The fact that the ganglion containing the neuron was completely isolated from all external influences demonstrates that the clock must be located within the neuron. Here we have positive evidence for the existence of a clock within a single cell.

C. Clock Mechanisms

At present we do not know anything about the anatomy of the clocks within the single cell—whether the clock is located in the nucleus, mitochondria, membranes, or in some enzyme systems. It is clear the periodic phenomena must in some way be programmed within the cell.

Further, we do not know whether the clock resembles the relaxation or pendulum types of periodic mechanisms as seen in various physical phenomena. Some information about this aspect may come from the study of the nature of the manifestations of the clock—the types of waves, etc. Thus, we see in the record of body temperature in Figure 57 of a patient with Hodgkin's disease that in each cycle body temperature increased at a steady rate to its maximum; then dropped off sharply to its originally low level. Most of the patients with the Pel-Ebstein syndrome of Hodgkin's disease show this type of record. This type of response would be expected

---

* Personal communication.

from a relaxation periodic mechanism.

In rats and in patients with some clinical entities, some clocks manifest themselves by sinusoidal curves and others by relaxation curves. Both types of curves may be present in the same individual at the same time. Thus, in the record of spontaneous activity and food intake of I^{131} treated rats in Figure 29 spontaneous activity showed a relaxation type of curve while food intake showed a sinusoidal type. In the records of the catatonic-schizophrenics in Figures 81 and 87 psychic state and spontaneous activity in bed showed relaxation type of curves; total nitrogen in urine, a clear-cut curve of a definitely sinusoidal type. Figure 87 also shows the record of an animal—one that showed cycles after prolonged treatment with sulfamerazine. Spontaneous running activity showed a relaxation type of curve; food-intake a sinusoidal type. It is quite possible that the difference in shapes of these curves may ultimately provide a basis for determining the temporal sequence between these two phenomena—spontaneous activity and nitrogen metabolism in patients, and spontaneous activity and food intake (presumably also, thus, of nitrogen metabolism) in the rat. Noteworthy is the inverse relationship between these latter two phenomena in Figures 29 and 87—that is, food intake is lowest on days of highest spontaneous activity.

Functions and Evolution of Clocks or Timing Devices

IT MUST BE pointed out again that none of the clocks that we know about at present can be consulted at any time of day or night. Thus they do not serve as chronometers as do our watches and clocks. These clocks signal only at the beginning of each phase or at the maxima and minima of sinusoidal curves.

So far as we know at the present, the only clock that has definitely useful functions measures time in twenty-four—or nearly twenty-four—hours. In rats it appears to have at least two functions:

1) to tell the animal at what time each day it can meet its mate or prey, or avoid its enemy; or at what time to emerge from its burrow on a dark day; or at what time it should return to the burrow at the end of the night.

2) to coordinate activity throughout the twenty-four hours with the functioning of the autonomic and emotional centers in the hypothalamus.

It is likely that at least some of the other clocks have one function in common: to provide periods of rest after activity.

It will not be possible in these lectures to speculate on evolution of the various clocks. I shall have to limit myself to a few general remarks.

First of all, it is now well established that one of the clocks—the twenty-four —or nearly twenty-four—hour clock, is present not only in man and other various mammals but also in plants, and in at least one unicellular organism *Euglena*.[96] This clock is controlled chiefly by light.

We know about cyclic changes in metabolism and behavior that seem to be controlled by the moon, tides and by annual changes in temperature. To what extent these clocks have become built into the organism and freed of outside control we do not know. Our observations on ground squirrels indicate that the presence in this animal of annual cycles of spontaneous running activity, food and water intake, and body weight, may have become "built-in," though still under control of light. Freed from this control by blinding, the clock apparently runs faster than before.

That many clocks have become submerged in one way or another during the process of evolution seems quite certain. Of interest is the observation that forty to fifty day clocks that appeared in the Norway rat only after various forms of experimental interference—exposure to severe stress—is still clearly present in normal desert rats. To what extent many of the clocks described in man and rodents will ultimately be traced back through lower organisms and how far—will only be known from long term studies on many intermediate forms.

Certainly it can be said that in the process of evolution man has progressively become more and more freed of periodic changes in functioning of individual organs, as well as in his total behavior—mood, etc., so that now normal man shows only slight, if any, diurnal variations; emotional changes associated with menstruation in normal women also are minimal.

Man differs in these respects from other primates—all of which give evidence of possessing regularly functioning clocks, particularly a twenty-four hour clock. All of our evidence indicates that light-active primates are almost exclusively active in the light and totally inactive in the dark. The twenty-four-hour clock undoubtedly plays an important part in their survival. In sharp contrast, man—for at least 350,000 years (according to Coon),[97] since he first discovered the use of fire, no longer has had the same need as other primates for a clock. Light from his hearth fire which was kept burning all night freed him of this need. In this way over the course of hundreds of thousands of

years, manifestation of man's clock have gradually become less and less profound, his survival depending more and more on smooth even performance around the twenty-four hours of the day, and according to our hypothesis the individual components of his clock have progressively become more out-of-phase with one another.

Part of the decrease in manifestations of cyclic phenomena in man and animals may have resulted as was postulated, from the progressive change to an out-of-phase relationship between individual components of the various clocks, and part from the development of inhibitory control of the clock by higher centers. As an example of the latter, we found in a number of instances that thyroid deficient rats that had failed to show cyclic changes, showed them very clearly after removal of the frontal poles of the brain. See Figure 102.

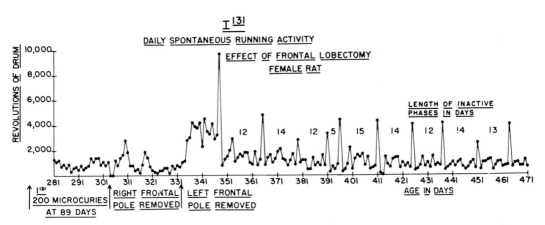

Figure 102. Graph demonstrating appearance of activity cycles in a I[131] treated rat after removal of the right and left frontal poles.[38]

Parts Played by Biological Clocks in Various Periodic Somatic and Mental Illnesses

WHAT PART DO biological clocks play in various periodic physical and mental illnesses? In attempting to answer this question I have reviewed histories of many hundreds of patients with all kinds of periodic illnesses.

A. Biological Clocks in Medicine and Psychiatry

In the scope of these lectures it will not be possible to present detailed histories of any of these patients. I shall have to restrict my remarks to a general summary of the results of these studies and a few overall conclusions.

In the first place, instances in which an illness manifests itself periodically are not common; they are, however, more common than would appear from the literature—since they are readily overlooked or not recognized by physicians. Patients showing periodic changes thus constitute only a small fraction of the total number of patients with any one of the following illnesses:

1) Hydrarthrosis.
2) Agranulocytosis.
3) Hodgkin's disease.
4) Catatonic-schizophrenia.

Furthermore, in most instances illnesses do not manifest themselves periodically at the outset, but only after many months or years. Intermittent hydrarthrosis seems exceptional, in that in some instances swelling produced by a blow on a joint is periodic from the outset. It is always possible, however, that the joint may actually not have been normal at the time of the trauma. We may conclude then that in nearly all instances, the simultaneous existence of two phenomena must be considered: 1) a basic illness, and 2) a periodic mechanism.

Our study has revealed existence of a definite relationship between these two phenomena—in that the periodicity, when it exists, recurrently in one phase exaggerates, then in the other phase reduces or eliminates the symptoms that were originally present—but does not bring out any new symptoms. This is clearly seen in many patients with forty-eight-hour clocks—with two phases each twenty-four hours in length. A manic patient will become more manic in one phase, and less manic or even normal in the other; a catatonic may become stuporous in one phase, less catatonic or even normal in the other; but neither patient will suddenly show fresh symptoms or other new developments. The appearance of the forty-eight-hour clock in otherwise mentally normal individuals was not associated with any mental or emotional symptoms—only strictly somatic symptoms—such, for instance, as fever.

On the basis of the shock-phase hypothesis we would explain the relationship between the basic illness and the clock in the following way: it must be assumed that: 1) before the appearance of the periodicity in an illness, the clock has been exercising control over brain centers or mechanisms responsible for the basic illness; 2) so long as individual units of the clock are out-of-phase the illness remains on a fairly constant level; 3) when, for one reason or another, the individual components of the clock come into phase, the illness shows correspondingly marked swings above and below its previous chronic level—the lengths of the intervals between the inherent rhythm of the individual components of the clock.

Thus, on this basis, it would seem questionable whether we are dealing with "periodic diseases"—but rather with periodic manifestations of basic illnesses. A catatonic-schizophrenic who has attacks regularly every twenty days is suffering primarily from catatonia-schizophrenia—the periodicity is incidental. Thus, we have numerous instances in which thyroid treatment has eliminated the cycles in periodic catatonic-schizophrenics, but the patients still remain catatonic-schizophrenic. However, owing to the great reduction in excursions of mood and behavior such patients are much more easy to handle and are often able even to resume some simple responsibilities.

Of special interest to psychiatrists are patients in whom the forty-eight-hour clock has manifested itself. In them we see most clearly the extent to which almost every symptom—physical, mental or emotional, and even the most complex personality function—is controlled and regulated by a clock in every case entirely independently of external influences and situations. We know of instances in which under the influence of the forty-eight-hour clock a schizophrenic became much more schizophrenic — even stuporous — in one twenty-four-hour phase and nearly normal in the other; or instances in which a depressed patient went into a much deeper depression, became suicidal in one twenty-four-hour phase and nearly normal in the other; or instances in which a patient underwent a complete personality change from one phase to another—living two separate lives on alternate days. Many such instances are described by Arndt[66] and Menninger-Lerchenthal.[5] This clock will be discussed in more detail in my monograph on the twenty-four—or nearly twenty-four—hour clock.

B. Adjustments of Patients to Periodic Illnesses

A number of patients with various forms of periodic illnesses have learned to live with, or have been helped to live with, their illnesses, so that they are able to carry on their work and normal activities.

A few examples will illustrate several such adjustments: 1) a star athlete at Cambridge University suffered from intermittent hydrarthrosis—his knees became swollen and very painful for two to three days every nine days. The attacks came with such a high degree of predictability that his team's schedule could be made out months ahead so as to avoid allowing the date of a game to coincide with swelling of his knees. As a matter of fact most patients with intermittent hydrarthrosis learn to live with their afflictions—partly because it usually is so strictly limited to the joints and has no mental or emotional accompaniments, and partly because in the intervals the joints are perfectly normal and show no signs of permanent damage. 2) A salesman with a forty-eight-hour clock was deeply depressed, unable to talk to anyone for twenty-four hours, and then became cheerful, outgoing, talkative for twenty-four hours. On depressed days he would drive up to a customer's office, be unable to get out of the car, and so sit there for hours, whereas on good days he was hail-fellow-well-met, outgoing, talkative, successful. On the appointment calendar which he showed me, alternate days were crossed out weeks ahead without appointments. In this way he managed to get along very well. 3) Mary Lamb, the sister of the great English writer, Charles Lamb, learned to live with a cyclic psychosis that persisted over fifty years of her life. At the age of thirty she had her first attack of mental illness lasting about one month. At the outset of her second attack two years later she killed her ailing mother of whom she had been very fond. Through the good offices of a barrister, a close friend of the family, she was not prosecuted and was put in custody of her brother, Charles, for life. She lived to be eighty-three and during her life had at least thirty-eight attacks—all of which required hospitalization. Figure 103 shows a record of these attacks.[98] The attacks occurred with regularity over some periods, and with little regularity in others—possibly owing in part

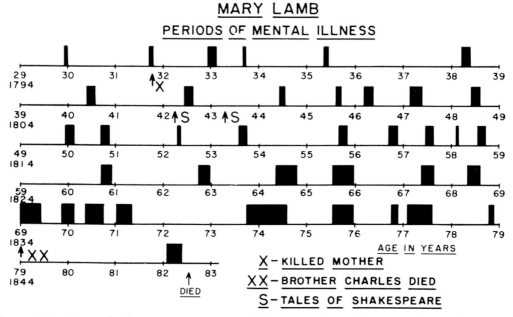

Figure 103. Bargraph showing occurrence and duration of psychotic attacks of the English writer, Mary Lamb (prepared from data collected by Ross[98]).

to failure of the records to show all of the attacks. According to the records, each attack ran a definite course starting and ending abruptly. Both Mary herself and her brother learned to recognize the very first signs of an oncoming attack—a slight irritability—and without further delay she was either rushed into a hospital or put into a straight jacket which they carried with them for emergency use. Immediately on recovering she returned home, entered into her normal rounds of entertaining their literary friends, collaborated with him in writing their books or their stories of Shakespeare's plays and so continued until the onset of the next attack. Of special interest is that despite this long series of illnesses she showed no signs of physical or mental deterioration other than those of old age.

C. Periodic Stigmata and Bleeding

One of the most interesting clocks in man measures weekly intervals between bleeding from stigmata. Many instances have been reported during the past few centuries of individuals—men and women—who bled on Thursday and Friday of each week from one part or another of the body, or from all parts from which Christ bled on the cross—the holes made by the nails in the palms and backs of the hands, soles and insteps of the feet, the holes made in the side of the chest by the soldier's lance, and the holes made in the scalp by the crown of thorns. Most of these individuals experienced trance-like states of ecstasy every Friday—during which they reported seeing, or in some way communicating with the Saviour, while they themselves suffered, often severe, pain referred to

the sites of the nails, thorns and spear wound. At the same time, in at least some instances, the affected individuals were entirely insensitive to pain from external stimuli; thus needles and pins could be pressed deep into the underlying muscle or laced through the skin and subcutaneous tissues without eliciting any evidence of pain. Occasionally these subjects showed manifestations of catalepsy.

Louise Lateau, a simple girl with little education, born in Belgium in 1850, was one of the most famous of these individuals. After an almost incredible series of serious illnesses and accidents, starting in her first month of life, at eighteen she suddenly developed severe pain in her left breast, from which she started to bleed every Friday. Subsequently she also began to bleed each Friday from all the sites from which Christ had bled on the cross. The stigmata continued their periodic appearances until her death in 1883.

This woman was examined over an eighteen month period by Dr. L. Lefebvre,[99] Professor of Pathology at the University of Louvain, as well as by eminent English physicians.

According to Schleyer,[100] author of a book on stigmata, Lefebvre was at first entirely convinced about the supernatural nature of the stigmata and ecstasy and wrote a book about them, but later made every effort to stop sale of the book and to recall all copies that had been sold.

Theresa Neumann was born in 1898 in Konnersreuth, near Munich, Germany. She was examined by many physicians and is perhaps the most famous of modern bearers of stigmata. Between the ages of twenty months and twenty-eight years she experienced a series of falls, each followed by many, often dramatic, complications. By twenty-eight she had recovered remarkably from the resultant blindness, deafness, contractures and paralyses. At this time she showed her first stigmata, bleeding from the left breast on Fridays. Like Louise Lateau, she gradually developed more and more stigmata, with bleeding occurring regularly Thursday night and Fridays, and accompanied by periods of ecstasy. She died in 1962 at the age of sixty-four.

Both women are of special interest not only in that they showed stigmata but at such regular seven-day intervals. Reimann has discussed the periodic nature of Theresa Neumann's stigmata in a paper read before the Association of American Physicians in 1957.[101] These women must have had seven-day clocks that manifested themselves in periodic bleeding. From our review of the literature we know that a seven-day clock has been seen in a number of individuals; that it may manifest itself in a variety of ways. Severe body trauma, exposure to high temperatures in these two women may have helped to free this seven- or nearly seven-day clock. We must recall here that the platelets have a life cycle near seven days. Whether the trauma could have damaged the platelet-forming cells in the bones we do not know. Further dietary deficiencies commonly present during the last century and early part of the present century might also account for a susceptibility to bleeding.

On the basis of our present knowledge we can conclude that the appearance of those stigmata would thus depend on: first of all, the presence of a seven- or nearly seven-day clock that manifests itself in periodic bleeding; and then on a high degree of suggestibility in a hysterical individual with a strong religious background.

D. Double Personalities

A number of patients have been described in the literature who harbor two quite different personalities in the two phases respectively of a forty-eight-hour clock.[5] They show one personality for alternate twenty-four-hour phases; and another for the other alternating phases; work and activity, etc. left unfinished at the end of one twenty-four-hour period were resumed twenty-four hours later.

We may thus consider the possibility that some of the Dr. Jekyll and Mr. Hyde personalities may actually have a definite neurological foundation.

E. Periodic Dipsomania

Of interest here are patients with periodic dipsomania who go on drinking sprees often at very regular intervals. It is very likely that these patients suffer from one or another of the periodic illnesses—ones particularly that bring about severe pain from which the patient finds that alcohol alone brings relief. In a dipsomaniac the temporal sequence of symptoms tends to remain almost exactly the same in many successive attacks. In many other ways the clocks closely resemble periodic manifestations of one or another of our clocks. These patients have been fully studied and discussed by Menninger-Lerchenthal.[5]

Of interest here are the results of preliminary experiments on alcohol appetites of rats in which long term cycles have been produced by one form or another of experimental interference. A number of these rats have shown clear-cut cyclical changes in alcohol appetite—but in inverse relationship to food and water intake—drinking more alcohol during the phase when they eat less food and drink less water and vice versa.

Biological Clocks in Normal Persons

ACCORDING TO THESE observations the human body harbors a number of timing devices that play important, but unseen, roles in the regulation and control not only of various somatic processes but of mental and emotional states as well.

These devices are located in various parts of the body—in different areas of the brain, in the endocrine and lymph glands, in bones, etc.; it seems very likely that every organ appears to be under the control of one or more of these clocks.

We know that these timing devices exist—chiefly from observations made on persons with one or another of the periodic illnesses; also from observations made on the appearance of periodic phenomena in animals after various forms of experimental interference with the brain, endocrine glands, and other organs.

Mystery that has long enshrouded periodic phenomena in man—especially in psychiatry—has now been dispelled by the observations that similar periodic phenomena can be produced in animals by various forms of experimental interference.

That these clocks are not recognizable in normal individuals was explained in terms of a "shock-phase" hypothesis. According to this hypothesis each individual component of a timing device —a cell, a follicle, etc., has its own inherent rhythm characteristic of the organ of which it forms a part. In a normally functioning organ these cells function more or less out-of-phase giving rise to an even performance of the organ. The inherent rhythm of the individual timing devices comes out only under pathological conditions in which the individual components are brought into phase.

The results of these observations and experiments indicate that important functions of the body are regulated not only by homeostatic mechanisms, but by probably much more primitive mechanisms, chiefly in the brain—mechanisms that function independently to a great extent of all internal and external influences.

One of the most important differences between man and apes and monkeys is that man exposed as he has been for several hundred thousand years to artificial light at night, through his use of fire, has been able to free himself from the twenty-four-hour, and possibly other clocks—which in apes and lower animals are rigidly adjusted to the light of day.

The existence of these timing devices may have been overlooked for so long because of the lengths of units in which they measure time—ranging from hours to months or even years.

To what extent functions of the various timing devices are interrelated is not known.

In general it can be said that any

marked cyclic manifestation in man indicates the presence of some kind of disturbance. A perfectly healthy well integrated person would not be expected to show any fluctuations in somatic or mental functions.

References

1. Richter, C. P.: Biological clocks in medicine and psychiatry: shock-phase hypothesis. *Proc. Nat. Acad. Sci., 46*:1506, 1960.

2. Richter, C. P.: A behavioristic study of the activity of the rat. *Comp. Psychol. Monog., 1*:1, 1922.

3. Pilcz, A.: *Die periodischen Geistes-*störungen. Verl. G. Fischer, Jena, 1901.

4. Gjessing, R.: Beiträge zur Kenntnis der Pathophysiologie des katatonen Stupors. I. Mitteilung: Über periodisch rezidivierenden katatonen Stupor, mit kritischem Beginn und Abschluss. *Arch. Psychiat.* 96:319, 1932.

   Beiträge zur Kenntnis der Pathophysiologie des katatonen Stupors. II. Mitteilung. Über aperiodisch rezidivierend verlaufenden katatonen Stupor mit lytischem Beginn und Abschluss. *Arch. Psychiat.* 96:393, 1932.

   Beiträge zur Kenntnis der Pathophysiologie der katatonen Erregung. III. Mitteilung. Über periodisch rezidivierende katatone Erregung, mit kritischem Beginn und Abschluss. *Arch. Psychiat.* 104:355, 1936.

5. Menninger-Lerchenthal, R.: *Periodizität in der Psychopathologie.* Bonn & Bern, Wien, 1960.

6. Reimann, H. A.: Periodic fever, an entity. A collection of 52 cases. *Am. J. Med. Sci., 243*:162, 1962.

7. Richter, C. P.: Animal behavior and internal drives. *Quart. Rev. Biol., 2*:307, 1927.

8. Munn, N. L.: *Handbook of Psychological Research on the Rat.* Houghton Mifflin Co., Boston, 1950.

9. Cold Spring Harbor Symposia on Quantitative Biology. *Biological Clocks,* 25: 1960. The Biological Laboratory, Cold Spring Harbor, L. I. New York. Printed by Waverly Press Inc., Baltimore, Md.

10. Johnson, M. S.: Activity and distribution of certain wild mice in relation to biotic communities. *J. Mammal., 7*:245, 1926.

11. Johnson, M. S.: Effect of continuous light on periodic spontanous activity of white-footed mice (Peromyscus). *J. Exp. Zool., 82*:315, 1939.

12. Rawson, K. S.: Homing behavior and endogenous activity rhythms. Ph.D. thesis, Harvard University, Cambridge, Massachusetts, 1956.

13. Rawson, K. S.: Effects of tissue temperature on mammalian activity rhythms. Cold Spring Harbor Symposia on Quantitative Biology. *Biological Clocks,* 25:105, 1960.

14. Bünning, E.: *Die Physiologische Uhr.* 2nd Edition. Springer, Berlin 1963.

15. Aschoff, J.: Exogenous and endogenous components in circadian rhythms. Cold Spring Harbor Symposia on Quantitative Biology. *Biological Clocks,* 25:11, 1960.

16. Pittendrigh, C. S.: Circadian rhythms and the circadian organization of living systems. Cold Spring Harbor Symposia on Quantitative Biology. *Biological Clocks,* 25: 159, 1960.

17. Bruce, V. G.: Environmental entrainment of circadian rhythms. Cold Spring Harbor Symposia on Quantitative Biology. *Biological Clocks,* 25:29, 1960.

18. Brown, F. A., Jr.: Response to pervasive geophysical factors and the biological clock problem. Cold Spring Harbor Symposia on Quantitative Biology. *Biological Clocks,* 25:57, 1960.

19. Halberg, F.: Temporal coordination of physiologic function. Cold Spring Harbor Symposia on Quantitative Biology. *Biological Clocks,* 25:289, 1960.

20. Harker, J. E.: Diurnal rhythms in the animal kingdom. *Biological Rev.,* 33:1, 1958.

21. Richter, C. P., and Wang, G. H.: New apparatus for measuring the spontaneous motility of animals. *J. Lab. & Clin. Med.,* 12:289, 1926.

22. Wang, G. H.: The relation between 'spontaneous' activity and oestrous cycle in the white rat. *Comp. Psychol. Monog.,* 2:1, 1923.

23. Long, J. A. and Evans, H. M.: The oestrous cycle in the rat and its associated phenomena. *Memoirs of the University of California,* 6:1, 1922. University of California. Press. Berkeley, California.

24. Haterius, H. O.: Partial sympathectomy and induction of pseudopregnancy. *Am. J. Physiol.,* 103:97, 1933.

25. Meyer, R. K., Leonard, S. L., and Hisaw, F. L.: Effect of anesthesia on artificial production of pseudopregnancy on the rat. *Proc. Soc. Exp. Biol. & Med.,* 27:340, 1929-1930.

26. Shelesnyak, M. C.: The induction of pseudopregnancy in the rat by means of electrical stimulation. *Anat. Rec.,* 49:179, 1931.

27. Selye, H., and McKeown, T.: Studies on the physiology of the maternal placenta in the rat. *Proc. Royal Soc. London,* 119:1, B, 1935.

28. Brouha, L.: Production of placentomata in rats injected with anterior hypophyseal fluid. *Proc. Soc. Biol. & Med.,* 25:488, 1927-1928.

29. Teel, H. M.: Effects of injecting anterior hypophysial fluid on the course of gestation in the rat. *Am. J. Physiol.,* 79:170, 1926-1927.

30. Taubenhaus, M., and Soskin, S.: Release of luteinizing hormone from the anterior hypophysis by an acetylcholine-like substance from the hypothalamic region. *Endocrinol.,* 29:958, 1941.

31. Swingle, W. W., Seay, P., Perlmutt, J., Collins, E. J., Barlow, G. Jr., and Fedor, E. J.: An experimental study of pseudopregnancy in rat. *Am. J. Physiol.,* 167:586, 1951.

32. Dury, A. , and Bradbury, J. T.: Copper-induced pseudopregnancy in the adult estrous rat. *Am. J. Physiol.,* 135:587, 1941.

33. Swingle, W. W., Fedor, E. J., Barlow, G. Jr., Collins, E. J. and Perlmutt, J.: Induction of pseudopregnancy in rat following adrenal removal. *Am. J. Physiol.,* 167:593, 1951.

34. Rosen, S., and Shelesnyak, M. C.: Induction of pseudopregnancy in rat by silver nitrate on nasal mucosa. *Proc. Soc. Exp. Biol. & Med.,* 36:832, 1937.

35. Harris, G. W.: The induction of pseudopregnancy in the rat by electrical stimulation through the head. *J. Physiol.,* 88:361, 1937.

36. Weichert, C. K., and Boyd, R. W.: Induction of typical pseudopregnancy in the albino rat by means of experimental hyperthyroidism. *Anat. Rec.,* 58:55, 1933-1934.

37. Richter, C. P.: Cyclical phenomena produced in rats by section of the pituitary stalk and their possible

relation to pesudopregnancy. *Am. J. Physiol., 106*:80, 1933.

38. Richter, C. P., Jones, G. S., and Biswanger, L.: Periodic phenomena and the thyroid. I. Abnormal but regular cycles in behavior and metabolism produced in rats by partial radiothyroidectomy. *Arch. Neurol. & Psychiat., 81*:233, 1959.

39. Richter, C. P.: The role played by the thyroid gland in the production of gross body activity. *Endocrinol., 17*:73, 1933.

40. Richter, C. P., Jones, G. S., and Woods, J. W.: Behavior cycles produced in rats by thyroidectomy, injection of I^{131} or by feeding sulfamerazine. Meeting of the Endocrine Society, May 28, 29 and 30, 1953. New York City.

41. Richter, C. P.: Hormones and rhythms in man and animals. *Recent Progress in Hormone Research, 13*: 105, 1957. (Ed. Gregory Pincus, Academic Press Inc., New York. 1957.)

42. Richter, C. P.: Experimental diabetes insipidus. *Brain, 53*:76, 1930.

43. Richter, C. P.: Lasting after-effects produced in rats by several commonly used drugs and hormones. *Proc. Nat. Acad. Sci., 45*:1080, 1959.

44. Shelesnyak, M. C.: Personal communication.

45. Richter, C. P., and Benjamin, J. A., Jr.: Ligation of the common bile duct in the rat. *Arch. Path., 18*: 817, 1934.

46. Pearson, C. M.: Development of arthritis in the rat following injection with adjuvant. Mechanisms of Hypersensitivity. International Symposium sponsored by the Henry Ford Hospital, Detroit, Michigan. Little Brown & Co., Boston, 1959.

47. Richter, C. P.: Phenomenon of sudden death in animals and man. *Psychosom. Med., 19*:191, 1957.

48. Wang, G. H., and Guttmacher, A. F.: The effects of ovarian traumatization on the spontaneous activity and genital tract of the albino rat, correlated with a histological study of the ovaries. *Am. J. Physiol., 82*: 335, 1927.

49. Wada, Tomi: An experimental study of hunger in its relation to activity. *Arch. Psychol.* Monograph, *57*:1, 1922.

50. Dement, W. C., and Kleitman, N.: Cyclic variations in EEG during sleep and their relation to eye movements, body motility, and dreaming. EEG *Clin. Neurophysiol., 9*:673, 1957.

51. Hitzig, W. H.: Periodische Krankheit. Kasuistische Mitteilung von vier typischen Fällen. *Hel. Paed. Acta, 10*:649, 1955.

52. Hoffman, A. M., and Probirs, F. W.: Intermittent hypothermia with disabling hyperhidrosis. *J. A. M. A., 120*:445, 1942.

53. Baker, B. M.: Undulant fever presenting the clinical syndrome of intemittent hydrarthrosis. *Arch. Int. Med., 44*:128, 1929.

54. Israel, J.: Über Fieber bei malignen Nieren- und Nebennierengeschwülsten. *Deutsche Med. Wochenschrift, 37*:57, 1911.

55. Hitzig, W. H., and Fanconi, G.: Das periodische Fieber und seine Differentialdiagnose. *Helv. Paed. Acta, 8*:326, 1953.

56. Cobet, R., and Schilling, V.: Periodisch-rezidivierende Neutropenie mit Monocytose. *Fol. Haematol., 70*:286, 1951.

57. Ebstein, W.: Das chronische Rückfallsfieber, eine neue Infections-

krankheit. *Berl. Klin. Wchnsch.*, *24*:565, 1887.

58. Demmer, T.: Morbus Maculosus Werlhofii in regelmässigen vierwöchentlichen Schüben bei einem 60 jährigen Mann nebst Untersuchungen über Blutplättchen. *Fol. Haemat.*, *26*:74, 1920-1921.

59. Timme, W.: Periodicity in endocrinopathic states. *J. Mt. Sinai Hosp.*, 9:818, 1942-1943.

60. Jahiel, R.: Concept of periodicity in the natural history of peptic ulcer and its consequences. *Am. J. Dig. Dis.*, *20*:257, 1953.

61. Leonard, K.: Eigenartige Tagesschwankugen des Zustandbildes bei Parkinsonismus. *Z. f. die ges. Neurol. & Psychiat.*, *134*:76, 1931.

62. Griffiths, G. M., and Fox, J. T.: Rhythm in Epilepsy. *Lancet*, 2: 409, 1938.

63. Langdon-Down, M., and Brain, W. R.: Time of day in relation to convulsions in epilepsy. *Lancet*, *216*: 1029, 1929.

64. Richter, C. P.: Two-day cycles of alternating good and bad behavior in psychotic patients. *Arch. Neurol. & Psychiat.*, *39*:587, 1938.

65. Bleuler, E.: *Handbuch der Psychiatrie* (G. Aschaffenburg) Spezieller Teil. Dementia-Praecox. Page 197, 1911.

66. Arndt, M.: Über täglichen (24 stündigen) Wechsel psychischer Krankheitszustände. *Allgem. Z. f. Psychiatrie*, *92*: 128, 1930.

67. Folin, O., and Shaffer, P. A.: On phosphate metabolism. *Am. J. Physiol.*, 7:135, 1902.

68. Richter, C. P.: Cyclic manifestations in the sleep curves of psychotic patients. *Arch. Neurol. & Psychiat.*, *31*:149, 1934.

69. Crammer, J. L.: Water and sodium in two psychotics. *Lancet*, *1*:1122, 1959.

70. Scheid, K. F.: *Febrile Episoden bei schizophrenen Psychosen.* Leipzig, 1937. Gg. Thieme Verlag.

71. Lindsay, J. S. B.: Periodic catatonia. *J. Ment. Sci.*, *94*:590, 1948.

72. Richter, C. P., Honeyman, W. M. and Hunter, H.: Behavior and mood cycles apparently related to parathyroid deficiency. *J. Neurol. & Psychiat.*, *3*:19, 1940.

73. Rice, K. K.: Regular forty to fifty day cycles of psychotic behavior in a 14-year-old boy. *Arch. Neurol. & Psychiat.*, *51*:478, 1944.

74. Kraepelin, E.: *Lehrbuch der Psychiatrie.* 8. Aufl., 3. Bd. J. A. Barth, Leipzig, 1913.

75. Reimann, H. A., and Angelides, A. P.: Periodic arthralgia in twenty-three members of five generations of a family. *J. A. M. A.*, *146*:713, 1951.

76. Reimann, H. A., Moadié, J., Semerdjian, S., and Sahyoun, P. F.: Periodic peritonitis—heredity and pathology. Report of seventy-two cases. *J. A. M. A.*, *154*:1254, 1954.

77. Starobinski, A.: Un cas de psychose maniaque-dépressive à un jour d'alternance. *Z. f. d. ges. Neurol. & Psychiat.*, *26*:295, 1921.

78. Näcke, P.: Raritäten aus der Irrenanstalt. *Allg. Z. f. Psychiat.*, *50*:630, 1894.

79. Stokes, A. B.: Problems of Schizophrenia. The Metabolic and Physiological Survey of a Case of Periodic Catatonia from Illness to Recovery. *Proc. Royal College of Physicians of Canada*, 1956.

80. Gornall, A. G., Eglitis, B., Miller, A., Stokes, A. B., and Dewan, J. G.: Long term clinical and metabolic observations in periodic catatonia. *Am. J. Psychiat.*, *109*:584, 1953.

81. Mall, G.: Beitrag zur Gjessingschen Thyroxinbehandlung der periodischen Katatonien. *Arch. f. Psychiat. & Nervenkrank, 187*:381, 1951-1952.

82. Lindsay, J. S. B.: Periodic catatonia. *J. Ment. Sci., 94*:590, 1948.

83. Arey, L. B.: The degree of normal menstrual irregularity. *Am. J. Obstet. & Gyn., 37*:12, 1939.

84. Garrod, A. E.: Concerning intermittent hydrarthrosis. *Quart. J. Med., 3*:207, 1910.

85. Kalmus, H.: Periodizität und Autochronie (Ideochronie) als zeitregelnde Eigenschaften der Organismen. *Biologia Generalis, 11*:93, 1935.

86. Pittendrigh, C. S., and Bruce, V. G.: Daily rhythms as coupled oscillator systems; and their relation to thermoperiodism and photoperiodism. In *Photoperiodism and Related Phenomena in Plants and Animals*. Ed. A. R. and R. Withrow. AAAS Publication #55, Washington, D.C. 1959.

87. Patt, H. M., and Maloney, M. A.: Control of granulocyte formation Brookhaven Symposia in Biology, #10, *Homeostatic Mechanisms*. Brookhaven National Laboratory, Upton, N. Y. 1957.

88. Hamilton, L. D.: Control of lymphocyte production. Brookhaven Symposia in Biology, #10, *Homeostatic Mechanisms*. Brookhaven National Laboratory, Upton, N. Y. 1957.

89. Cronkite, E.P.: Regulation of platelet production. Brookhaven Symposia in Biology, #10, *Homeostatic Mechanisms*. Brookhaven National Laboratory, Upton, N. Y. 1957.

90. Williams, R. G.: Microscopic studies of living thyroid follicles implanted in transparent chambers installed in the rabbit's ear. *Am. J. Anat., 62*:1, 1937-1938.

91. Bradford, N. M., and Davies, R. E.: The site of hydrochloric acid production in the stomach as determined by indicators. *Biochem. J., 46*:414, 1950.

92. Smith, H. W.: *Principles of Renal Physiology*. New York, Oxford University Press, 1956.

93. Franck, U. F.: Models for biological excitation processes. *Progress of Biophysics and Biophysical Chem., 6*:171, 1956.

94. Strumwasser, F., Smith, J. L., Gilliam, J. J., and Schlechte, F. R.: Indentification of active brain regions involved in the processes of hibernation. *XVI Inter. Congress of Zool., 2*:53, 1963.

95. Strumwasser, F.: A circadian rhythm of activity and its endogenous origin in a neuron. *Fed. Proc., 22*: 220, 1963.

96. Pohl, R.: Tagesrhythmus im phototaktischen Verhalten der *Euglena gracilis*. *Z. Naturforsch., 3b*:367, 1948.

97. Coon, C. S.: *The Origin of Races*. Alfred A. Knopf, New York, 1962.

98. Ross, E. C.: *The Ordeal of Bridget Elia. A Chronicle of the Lambs*. University of Oklahoma Press, Norman, Oklahoma, 1940.

99. Lefebvre, F.: *Louise Lateau*. Louvain, 1870.

100. Schleyer, F. L.: *Die Stigmatisation mit den Blutmalen*. Schmorl & von Seefeld Nachf., Hannover, 1948.

101. Reimann, H. A.: The case of Theresa Neuman of Konnenreuth: Stigmatism and its medical counterpart. 70th Annual meeting of the Assoc. Am. Physicians, 1957.

Index

Lectures Published in This Series